Assessment of Older Adults

With Diminished Capacity:

A Handbook for Psychologists

American Bar Association/American Psychological Association

Assessment of Capacity in Older Adults

Project Working Group

Defending Liberty Pursuing Justice

American Bar Association Commission on Law and Aging

740 15th Street, NW
Washington, DC 20005-1019

AMERICAN PSYCHOLOGICAL ASSOCIATION

750 First Street, NE
Washington, DC 20002-4242

About the American Bar Association Commission on Law and Aging

The mission of the American Bar Association (ABA) Commission on Law and Aging is to strengthen and secure the legal rights, dignity, autonomy, quality of life, and quality of care of elders. It carries out this mission through research, policy development, technical assistance, advocacy, education, and training. The ABA Commission consists of a 15-member interdisciplinary body of experts in aging and law, including lawyers, judges, health and social services professionals, academics, and advocates. With its professional staff, the ABA Commission examines a wide range of law-related issues, including: legal services to older persons; health and long-term care; housing needs; professional ethical issues; Social Security, Medicare, Medicaid, and other public benefit programs; planning for incapacity; guardianship; elder abuse; health care decision-making; pain management and end-of-life care; dispute resolution; and court-related needs of older persons with disabilities.

About the American Psychological Association

The American Psychological Association (APA) is the largest scientific and professional organization representing psychology in the United States and is the world's largest association of psychologists. Through its divisions in 53 subfields of psychology and affiliations with 59 state, territorial, and Canadian provincial associations, APA works to advance psychology as a science, as a profession, and as a means of promoting health, education, and human welfare. The APA Office on Aging coordinates the association's activities pertaining to aging and geropsychology (the field within psychology devoted to older adult issues). The Committee on Aging (CONA) is the committee within the APA governance structure dedicated to aging issues. Its six expert geropsychologists are selected for three-year terms. Together, the Office on Aging, CONA, and association members promote the health and wellbeing of older adults and their families through expanded scientific understanding of adult development and aging and the delivery of appropriate psychological services to older adults.

Disclaimer

The views expressed in this document have not been approved by the governing or policy-setting bodies of the American Bar Association or the American Psychological Association and should not be construed as representing policy of these organizations. Materials in this book were developed based on the consensus of a working group. **This document is not intended to establish a standard of practice against which clinical practice is to be evaluated. Rather, it provides a framework that psychologists may find useful and effective in capacity determination.** Although the principles presented herein are intended to be generally relevant across all legal jurisdictions, law and practice differ across state jurisdictions and sometimes even across county lines. **Thus, this book is intended to supplement (and cannot substitute for) a psychologist's working knowledge of relevant capacity law specific to his/her jurisdiction.** This book focuses on issues in civil capacity determination in older adults, not all aspects of capacity evaluation or all populations.

10 Digit ISBN Number: **1-60442-234-3**
13 Digit ISBN Number: **978-1-60442-234-4**
ABA Product Code: **4280029**

Table of Contents

Appendices

Available online at http://www.apa.org/pi/aging/capacity_psychologist_handbook.pdf

Acknowledgements

This book is the result of a collaborative effort of members of the American Bar Association (ABA) Commission on Law and Aging and the American Psychological Association (APA).

Assessment of Older Adults with Diminished Capacity: A Handbook for Psychologists is the third work product of the ABA/APA Assessment of Capacity in Older Adults Project Working Group, established in 2003 under the auspices of the interdisciplinary Task Force on Facilitating APA/ABA Relations. The first work product, *Assessment of Older Adults with Diminished Capacity: A Handbook for Lawyers* was published in 2005. The second product, *Judicial Determination of Capacity of Older Adults in Guardianship Proceedings: A Handbook for Judges* was published in 2006. Copies of both handbooks are available online at www.apa.org/pi/aging and www.abanet.org/aging.

Members of the ABA/APA Working Group for this project are: Barry Edelstein, PhD; Peter Lichtenberg, PhD, ABPP; Daniel Marson, JD, PhD; Jennifer Moye, PhD; David Powers, PhD; Charles Sabatino, JD; Aida Saldivar, PhD, ABPP; Erica Wood, JD; Stacey Wood, PhD; and Deborah DiGilio, MPH. Stacey Wood, PhD, and Jennifer Moye, PhD, are the editors of the psychologist's handbook.

Special contributors to this handbook include: Angela Jefferson, PhD (research consent capacity); Michele Karel, PhD, and Brian Carpenter, PhD (values); Lori Stiegel, JD (elder abuse and undue influence); and Susan Bernatz, PhD (undue influence). We thank Susie Hwang and Jamie Philpotts for their superb editorial assistance.

This handbook was reviewed by an advisory panel of psychologists convened for this project: Norman Abeles, PhD; Rebecca Allen, PhD; Adam M. Brickman, PhD; Michelle Braun, PhD; Brian D. Carpenter, PhD; Gordon J. Chelune, PhD, ABPP (CN); Eric Y. Drogin, JD, PhD, ABPP; Colleen Fairbanks, PhD; Michelle Dawn Gagnon, PsyD; Randy Georgemiller, PhD; Thomas Grisso, PhD; Irving Hellman, PhD; Bret Hicken, PhD; Leon Hyer, PhD; Angela L. Jefferson, PhD; Sayaka Machizawa, PsyD; Joseph R. Miles, MA; Barton W. Palmer, PhD; Sara Honn Qualls, PhD; Cheryl L. Shigaki, PhD, ABPP; and Martin Zehr, PhD. The handbook also was reviewed by Barbara Soniat, PhD, Arthur R. Derse, MD, JD and Kathleen Wilber, PhD, members of the ABA Commission on Law and Aging.

Finally, we thank the Borchard Foundation Center on Law and Aging for its financial support of this project.

Executive Summary

The ABA-APA Working Group on the Assessment of Capacity in Older Adults was established in 2003 under the auspices of the Task Force on Facilitating ABA-APA Relations. The workgroup has produced two volumes thus far, a handbook for attorneys and a handbook for judges. The current volume is designed for psychologists evaluating civil capacities of older adults. Contemporary probate law encourages functional assessments that describe task-specific deficits rather than global findings. With training in standardized cognitive and functional assessment, psychologists are in an ideal position to provide such evaluations.

The specific goal of this handbook is to review psychological assessment of six civil capacities of particular importance to older adults, namely, medical consent capacity, sexual consent capacity, financial capacity, testamentary capacity, capacity to drive, and capacity to live independently. The handbook also addresses the important topic of undue influence and introduces emerging areas of interest, such as the capacity to mediate, the capacity to participate in research, and the capacity to vote.

The handbook begins with an Overview Chapter that discusses the history of the workgroup, scope of the handbook, the increasing need for clinicians skilled in capacity assessment, as well as essential definitions. In Chapter 2, critical legal definitions of civil capacities are delineated. The chapter concludes by highlighting key differences between how the law views capacity and how psychologists view capacity.

Chapter 3 lays out a nine-part framework for conceptualizing capacity assessments. The framework expands on Thomas Grisso's conceptual model as it has evolved through discussion among working group members. Nine conceptual elements for conducting a capacity assessment are:

(1) identifying the applicable legal standard(s)
(2) identifying and evaluating functional elements constituent to the capacity
(3) determining relevant medical and psychiatric diagnoses contributing to incapacity
(4) evaluating cognitive functioning
(5) considering psychiatric and/or emotional factors
(6) appreciating the individual's values
(7) identifying risks related to the individual and situation
(8) considering means to enhance the individual's capacity
(9) making a clinical judgment of capacity.

A worksheet highlighting each of the elements is included in the handbook.

The next two chapters, Chapter 4 and Chapter 5, move away from theoretical models and provide more practical guidance to the clinician. Chapter 4 addresses important pre-assessment considerations including understanding the "who," "what," "why," and "when" of a particular capacity referral. In general, capacity evaluations require a more extensive "pre-assessment" process; this chapter provides information regarding what type of data should be collected prior to meeting the older adult. It further discusses the various roles a psychologist may play as an expert in these types of cases. Chapter 5 provides an overview of functional, cognitive, and behavioral assessment tools that may be used in capacity evaluations, with the understanding that there is no "capacimeter" or standardized battery that will work for all cases. The chapter concludes with suggestions for the integrating data, presenting results, and the importance of articulating a specific capacity opinion. Brief case examples are provided here, as well as a worksheet to assist clinicians in organizing the assessment process.

Chapter 6 covers in depth the assessment of each of the six specific capacities (medical consent capacity, sexual consent capacity, financial capacity, testamentary capacity, capacity to drive, and capacity to live independently). Each section reviews up-to-date relevant clinical literature and relevant assessment tools, walking through the nine-part framework in light of that specific capacity. An example report of a case is given for each of the specific capacities.

Chapter 7 introduces the related but also distinct concept of undue influence to the reader. Undue influence is a legal construct which refers to a dynamic in a confidential relationship where a stronger party exploits their influence of a weaker party, often for financial gain. This chapter covers legal definitions, clinical frameworks, and an assessment strategy for psychologists working with older adults that are potentially at risk or the victims of undue influence. A case example is provided.

Chapter 8 provides psychologists with practical advice for working with attorneys and the courts on matters related to capacity cases. This chapter will help psychologists connect with attorneys and be better prepared to provide the type of information most relevant legal professionals. The chapter also provides suggestions to the novice providing expert testimony in court and includes additional resources for those practitioners wanting more than an overview.

In Chapter 9 emerging capacity areas are introduced. These include the capacity to consent to research, the capacity to mediate, and the capacity to vote. These sections overview relevant literature but do not provide case examples.

In summary, the handbook seeks to provide a relatively concise yet also comprehensive reference in the area of civil capacity assessment of older adults by psychologists. Relevant literature, suggestions for assessment tools, and case examples are provided throughout the handbook. The members of the workgroup have enjoyed assembling this handbook and it is our hope that it will serve as a valuable resource and tool for psychologists throughout the United States and elsewhere.

I. The Importance of Psychological Assessment of Capacities

Robert Olsen is 89 years old and lives alone. One day he calls 911 because he feels ill and has fallen on the floor. The emergency medical personnel transport him to the hospital, noting that he is confused, unbathed, and his home is dirty, with spoiled food, urine, and feces in the house. They also found medications in disarray and empty beer bottles. Mr. Olsen is hospitalized for treatment for acute renal failure with malnutrition and dehydration. With medical intervention, his cognition clears considerably. However, there are residual problems with memory and reasoning. A brain scan shows no acute problems but a mild degree of cerebrovascular disease. Mr. Olsen reports anxiety in the hospital. He asks to be discharged and assures the team he can manage his medications, personal care, and meals. He expresses discomfort with home care services. Mr. Olsen values his independence and wants to return to his home of 63 years. The medical team asks the psychologist is he competent?

Clinical and legal professionals are increasingly turning to psychologists for opinions regarding the decision-making capacity of older adults, such as the case of Mr. Olsen. Often these complex cases require fine-grained cognitive and functional evaluation that balances promoting autonomy while protecting a vulnerable adult from harm. Psychologists are well-positioned to bring the critical skills of standardized assessment and comprehensive report writing to questions of diminished capacity. However, few psychologists receive formal training in capacity assessment of older adults and may be hesitant to take on these types of cases. The first time a psychologist is confronted with such a task, many questions may arise:

- Who do I talk to before the assessment?
- Is an attorney always involved?
- What does it mean to say someone lacks capacity?
- What is the family's role?
- What happens to the report?
- Should I use a cognitive test battery—which one?
- Do I need to use objective capacity measures—what are they?
- How do I approach the patient?
- How does the person's history and values figure in—what about the way he or she has always lived or made decisions?
- Do the choices reflect personal preferences or cultural differences?
- How do I integrate all the data to arrive at a definitive capacity judgment?
- How do I phrase my findings so they will be understandable to the non-psychologist?

The purpose of this handbook is to provide a resource to psychologists who are faced with such questions as they assess various capacities of older adults.

Scope of This Handbook

This handbook focuses on the assessment of "civil" capacities in older adults in medical, long term care, and private-practice settings. Six capacity domains are presented: medical consent, sexual consent, financial, testamentary, driving, and independent living capacities. In addition, the handbook discusses undue influence and the relationship of capacity assessment to legal interventions, such as guardianship or conservatorship. This handbook does not address capacities for criminal matters, such as the capacity to stand trial, capacity to represent oneself in a legal case, or capacity to be executed. However, at times questions regarding civil capacity arise in a criminal setting, for example, when an individual has perpetrated financial fraud against a vulnerable older adult, and the prosecuting or defense attorney is seeking information about the older adult's capacity to make financial decisions. The capacity is still "civil," although it is being referred to the psychologist in a criminal matter. This handbook is designed to address capacity assessment generally across the United States, but it is critical to be aware of the laws in one's own state. Some states may have provisions that differ from those in this handbook.

For definitions of legal terms common in civil capacity see **Appendix A.**

Purpose of Handbook

The purpose of the handbook is to promote sound assessment of older adults, which lead to appropriate interventions that balance promotion of autonomy and protection from harm. *This handbook is not a practice guideline and is not intended to establish a standard against which clinical practice is to be evaluated.* Rather, this handbook provides a framework and assessment examples that psychologists may find useful and effective in capacity evaluation. This is a handbook—with a goal of brevity and utility— and is not meant to serve as an exhaustive text on the matter of capacity assessment.

Working Group and Advisory Panel

The ABA/APA Working Group on the Assessment of Capacity in Older Adults was established in 2003 under the auspices of the Task Force on Facilitating ABA/APA Relations. The original working group was comprised of three members of the American Bar Association (ABA) Commission on Law and Aging and six members of the American Psychological Association (APA). When the working group convened for the current project, two new members were sought to replace two who had departed. Individuals were recruited who had expertise in the field (as evidenced through

clinical work and scholarship), with consideration of enhancing gender and ethnic diversity of the working group.

The working group developed an outline for the book, selected editors, and assigned chapter authors. Individual working group members then developed chapters and revised them based on extensive feedback from the group.

After an initial draft was completed, the handbook was shared with an advisory panel of 22 psychologists as well as representatives from the ABA Commission on Law and Aging. Advisory panel members were selected based on experience in the field of capacity assessment, and to represent a range of clinical settings and interest areas (e.g., geropsychology, forensic psychology, neuropsychology, and rehabilitation psychology). The advisory panel provided feedback on each chapter, which was collated and considered during conference calls by the working group. When feedback was discrepant, the working group made revisions to reflect the diversity of opinions in the field. This handbook is a product of the ABA/APA working group. It has not been approved by the governing or policy-setting bodies, and does not represent policy of the ABA or APA.

American Bar Association and the American Psychological Association Collaboration

The ABA Commission on Law and Aging and the APA have been collaborating to prepare clinical and legal professionals to meet the needs of the aging population. This educational handbook is one product of the collaboration, along with similar handbooks for lawyers and judges. These collaborative projects arose because psychologists within APA and legal professionals within ABA were seeking more information about capacity assessment of older adults. In addition to educating the respective memberships of these organizations, another important goal is to improve the manner that clinicians, lawyers, and judges communicate with each other about capacity matters.

The Handbook for Lawyers is at:
http://www.apa.org/pi/aging/capacity_lawyers_handbook.pdf

The Handbook for Judges is at:
http://www.apa.org/pi/aging/capacity_judges_handbook.pdf

Professional Competencies for Capacity Evaluation

Some psychologists may ask: is it necessary to be a forensic psychologist to do capacity assessment of older adults? A neuropsychologist? A geropsychologist? Because questions of civil capacities arise in a wide variety of settings and case particulars, there is no one right answer.

Capacity assessment referrals can come from a variety of sources and occur in a variety of settings that influence the approach taken to evaluation, and the professional competencies needed. For example, a request for an assessment of driving capacity may come from a family member and not involve a lawyer in any way. An assessment of capacity to make health care decisions may be requested by a physician. The knowledge base needed to address capacity issues in a frail, medically complex older adult living in a nursing home with many healthcare and family system issues is different from the knowledge base needed to assess a medically healthy but psychiatrically ill older adult who is referred by a court in a guardianship proceeding. For example, with Mr. Olsen, the case would benefit from a psychologist with a background in geriatric syndromes, gero-neuropsychological assessment, medical psychology, and aging services.

A psychologist will need to investigate the referral to determine if he or she has the professional competence to address the referral question based on education, training, supervised experience, consultation, or study as required by the *Ethical Principles of Psychologists and Code of Conduct* (APA, 2002).

This handbook may aid psychologists in their approach to capacity evaluation, but psychologists who are new to the assessment of capacity in older adults are encouraged to consult with colleagues or pursue additional education, training, and supervision in the area.

This handbook focuses on capacity assessment of older adults, and *presumes general competencies in the assessment of older adults*, such as selection of appropriately age-normed and validated tests, adaptation of assessment approaches, and knowledge of syndromes of aging. Psychologists seeking general resources about working with older adults may refer to the *Guidelines for Psychological Practice with Older Adults* (APA 2003, at www.apa.org/practice/adult.pdf) and other resources at the APA Office on Aging Web site www.apa.org/pi/aging.

Cultural Considerations

Cultural issues are of special concern in capacity assessment. With persons of diverse cultural background and experience, consideration needs to be given to the role of cultural variables in decision making. Cultural variables such as language, immigrant status, economical status, perceptions of institutions such as hospitals, as well as perceptions of disability and the role of family in care and decision making, are important. Consistent with the *Ethical Principles of Psychologists and Code of Conduct (APA, 2002)* practitioners need to be aware of test bias, test fairness, and cultural equivalence. For additional guidance in working with diverse populations refer to the *Guidelines on Multicultural Education, Training, Research, Practice, and Organizational Change for Psychologists* (APA, 2002 at http://www.apa.org/-pi/multiculturalguidelines). The intersection of cultural issues, values, and capacity assessment is further discussed in relevant sections of this handbook and in other sources (e.g., Qualls & Smyer, 2007).

Age Considerations

An evaluation of capacity may be utilized to resolve critical disagreements about individual decisions, and the need to offer protection versus to promote autonomy. In a civil capacity evaluation, these decisions may be about the most personal matters in one's life: what procedures will be done to your body, where you will live, who you are intimate with, how you spend your money. All persons are presumed to have capacity, and, when this is so, have the "right to folly" – that is – have the right to make "bad" decisions. The psychologist performing a civil capacity evaluation is often addressing just this issue: is this person making a decision we disagree with, but one we must respect because the person has capacity, or, because this person lacks the capacity to make the decision, must we step in to protect him or her. In these situations, psychologists may need to guard against ageism in themselves and others. An obvious point, but one worth stating, is that age itself does not imply diminished capacity or greater "permission" to be protective or paternalistic. Instead, an objective assessment of capacity, including the risks of the situation, is required. As will be discussed in later sections of the book, consideration must be given to whether the risks associated with the decision are new or long-standing, and whether the risks are serious and likely to happen.

The Need to Focus on Older Adults

Capacity assessment of older adults is increasing. The older adult population will double between 2000 and 2030, to 71.5 million adults over the age of 65 (Wan, Sengupta, Velkoff, & DeBarros, 2005). The fastest growing group of older adults is the 85+ age range, which is expected to grow from 4.2 million in 2000 to 12.9 million by 2020, an over two hundred percent increase (Administration on Aging, 2006). While most older adults do not have dementia, older adults as a group are at higher risk for cognitive impairment than younger adults. An estimated 5.2 million Americans of all ages have Alzheimer's disease in 2008. The number of people age 65 and over with Alzheimer's disease is estimated to reach 7.7 million in 2030 (Alzheimer's Association, 2008). These factors will result in an increasing demand for assessment of the capacities of older adults.

Evolution of the Field

Historically, evaluations of decisional capacity have been made on the basis of a clinical interview or general mental status evaluation. Such clinical evaluations can be unreliable (Markson, 1994; Marson, McInturff, Hawkins, Bartolucci, & Harrell, 1997; Rutman & Silberfeld, 1992). Personal values, experience in the field, and ageism may influence a clinician's risk tolerance and his or her view of an older adult's decisional capacity (Clemens & Hayes, 1997). Clinicians from theoretical orientation and professional backgrounds may differ in their evaluations of capacity. For example, feedback from our own advisory panel revealed differing opinions about the case of Mr. Olsen.

While the use of standardized psychological and neuropsychological tests may improve the reliability of capacity assessment, validity may still suffer. It can be unclear how to relate general psychological assessment data (e.g., "impaired immediate memory") to specific capacity questions ("capacity to make a will"). Clinicians focus on different cognitive abilities in predicting capacity (Marson, Hawkins, McInturff, & Harrell, 1997).

Forensic Assessment Instruments

A major advance in the field has been the development of instruments to assess specific functional abilities relevant to legal capacities, what Thomas Grisso refers to as "forensic assessment instruments." Many of these instruments are described in detail in his book *Evaluating Competencies, 2nd ed.* (2003), as well as in other sources (Moye, Gurrera, Karel, Edelstein, & O'Connell, 2005; Qualls & Smyer, 2007; Sturman, 2005), and are summarized in Appendix B of this handbook. For example, the evaluation of Mr. Olsen would best be accomplished by directly assessing functions necessary to independent living.

Some specific capacity areas, such as medical consent capacity, have seen a great deal of instrument development, while others have seen little to none, such as sexual consent capacity and testamentary capacity. While these instruments represent an extremely important advancement of the field, most lack adequate reliability, validity, and normative properties for older adults. They are further discussed in relevant sections of Chapter 6.

Capacity Research

Another important advance in the field has been the emergence of the field of capacity as a distinct field of legal, clinical, and behavioral research (Marson & Ingram, 1996). The origins of the field lie in a series of seminal articles (Appelbaum, 1982; Appelbaum & Bateman, 1980; Appelbaum & Grisso, 1988; Appelbaum & Roth, 1981; Meisel, Roth, & Lidz, 1977; Roth, Meisel, & Lidz, 1977), and work by Appelbaum and Grisso (Appelbaum et al., 1988; Appelbaum & Grisso, 1995; Grisso, 1986; Grisso & Applebaum, 1998), and of others focusing on older adults (Fitten, Lusky, & Hamann, 1990; Kim & Caine, 2002; Marson, Chatterjee, Ingram, & Harrell, 1996; Marson, Cody, Ingram, & Harrell, 1995; Moye & Karel, 1999; Sabatino, 1996; Smyer, Schaie, & Kapp, 1996; Stanley, Stanley, Guido, & Garvin, 1988; Taub, Baker, Kline, & Sturr, 1987), which advanced the theoretical and empirical basis of the field of civil capacity assessment. However, the body of capacity research dedicated to older adults is modest and remains a rich area for future research to guide this expanding and complex area of clinical practice.

Why Are Evaluations of Capacity in Older Adults Challenging?

Cases Involving Older Adults Are Complex

When an older adult is referred to a psychologist for an evaluation there often are many layers of complexity to consider. Consider the example of Robert Olsen: at first glance he appears to have significant decisional and functional impairments apparent from the facts of his living situation. But what do we really know about Mr. Olsen.

Does he have family or friends? What is important to him? Why is he anxious? Is his anxiety in need of treatment? Is he drinking in excess or in a manner that conflicts with medications? Does he know this? Are all his doctors aware of what other doctors are prescribing? Is the medication schedule simple enough to follow? Is there a way to offer supportive services to him that is less threatening? Are his cardiac or pulmonary conditions treated? Do the infarcts seen on the brain scan translate to meaningful deficits? Has his delirium resolved? Can any interventions improve his functioning? Can he see and hear? Is he depressed? Has someone close to him died?

As we learn more about Mr. Olsen, the list of questions may extend further. Clinical evaluation of older adults is complex because older adults are exceedingly complex—with a lifetime of psychological, social, cultural, and biological factors that contribute to the individual's specific strengths, weaknesses, social system, lifestyle, and values. Because of this it is important to develop knowledge and skills in evaluating and treating older adults.

Capacity Assessment Is a New Practice Area for Psychologists

At an earlier time, clinical capacity determination was generally left to physicians. The involvement of psychologists is more recent. As such, some psychologists may be unfamiliar with the meaning of the term capacity or the wide range of interventions that may apply to an older adult with decisional or functional impairments. These include the appointment of a guardian, conservator, healthcare proxy, durable power of attorney, or representative payee, as well as more social or clinical interventions—for example, bill paying programs through elder services.

> Legal and social interventions for functional impairments are described in **Appendix F.**

Psychologists are routinely trained in psychological and cognitive assessment, but rarely in the specifics of capacity assessment. For example, the psychologist may be unsure of what data are necessary to answer the question "does this person have the capacity to manage finances?"

Confusion About the Term Capacity

Many psychologists may be more familiar with the term *competency* rather than *capacity*. Some recommend the term competency be used only to refer to a legal finding, with the term capacity to refer to clinical findings. While this is an excellent practice as far as it goes, it only goes so far, since many practitioners do not abide by the distinction. In practice many clinicians still refer to a patient's "competency," leading to ongoing confusion. *One approach to avoid confusion is to simply adopt the phrase legal capaci ty and clin ical capacity.*

Some use the term *decision-making capacity* interchangeably with capacity, or to describe capacity domains that are specifically and only decisional in nature. That is, a distinction may be drawn between decisional capacity (the capacity to decide) versus executional capacity (the capacity to implement a decision) (Collopy, 1988). For example, the capacity to make a health care decision may only involve cognitive processes of deciding, whereas the capacity to manage finances may involve making decisions and executing actions in concordance with decisions (e.g., balancing a checkbook). Importantly, the mere presence of physical inability and loss of "executional capacity" does not constitute incapacity, as the individual who retains decisional capacity may direct another to perform the task.

More on legal definitions of capacity is in **Chapter 2.**

Another distinction may be drawn between *global capacity* versus *specific capacities*. Both clinical and legal professionals have used the term "competency" to refer to a person's global ability to engage in a wide range of functions. It has traditionally been thought of as categorical—an individual either is competent or is not. However, within the global application of the term competency, there was little if any consideration of: (a) the ability to successfully perform specific functions; (b) intra-individual variance in performance across functional domains; or (c) potential methods of enhancing an individual's ability to perform a given function or functions.

Currently, the emphasis is shifting in both clinical and legal settings to the use of the term capacities to allow a focus on the specific functional capacities, and means of maximizing those capacities. This shift can be seen in civil law, particularly in guardianship[1] and other surrogate decision-making areas in a preference for the term capacity. Guardianship is a relationship created by state law in which a court gives one person or entity (the guardian) the duty and power to make personal and/or property decisions for another (the incapacitated person) upon a court finding that an adult lacks capacity to make decisions for him or herself.

When a petition for guardianship is filed, psychologists may be asked to evaluate a broader set of capacities—can this person be independently responsible for his or her life? However, this question still does not translate into all-or-none "competency." Psychologists providing evaluations will offer a great deal to the courts by assessing specific domains, and identifying areas of retained strengths, which will enable the judge to craft a "limited order," that is, to limit the authority of the guardian to only those areas where the person needs assistance (American Bar Association Commission on Law and Aging et al., 2006).

Confusion from Referring Parties

A national survey of 395 psychiatrists, geriatricians, and geriatric psychologists (Ganzini, Volicer, Nelson, & Derse, 2003), noted that requests for capacity evaluation were frequently associated with misunderstanding or "myths" about capacity and the role of capacity assessment. These myths include: equating legal

---

[1] States use various terms for guardianship of the person and guardianship of property. For example, some use the term conservatorship either generically or to indicate guardianship of property. Check state law. This handbook refers to guardianship generically as encompassing authority over personal and/or property decisions, unless otherwise indicated.

and clinical capacity; assuming a lack of capacity when patients go against medical advice; confusing involuntary civil commitment with incapacity.

These continuing myths mean the psychologist often has to investigate, clarify, and re-formulate a capacity evaluation request before beginning the evaluation. Psychologists who are new to capacity evaluation may find the ongoing misunderstanding about capacity to increase their own confusion. This may account for the low reliability noted in assessment of capacity (Marson et al., 1997), which is improved when clinicians are educated about capacity (Marson, Earnst, Jamil, Bartolucci, & Harell, 2000).

In the case of Mr. Olsen, the team asks for an evaluation of "competency." Does the team mean capacity? Capacity for what? Is the team interested in clinical or legal capacity? Is there an intended course of action—such as pursuing a guardianship or nursing home placement? Have less restrictive alternatives been explored?

Multiple Roles

Although the referral question may be "assess for capacity," it is often up to the evaluator to determine the specific role that he or she will play in each case. In the case of Mr. Olsen, the referring question may be to complete an evaluation of his capacity to live independently.

However, the psychologist may decide that such an assessment should be delayed, if possible, until after a rehabilitation stay in which Mr. Olsen can regain function, can have his anxiety treated, and to allow for the possibility of developing in-home services that are comfortable and appropriate for Mr. Olsen.

As illustrated in this case, the psychologist must then balance the role of promoting self-determination, addressing the functional deficit, and providing recommendations to clinical and legal professionals involved with the person. Special attention should be paid to means to maximize the functional capacity of the individual. Thus, a thoughtful evaluator may

find that an older adult who does not have the capacity to perform a specific function at the moment of evaluation may have insight and can delegate to another with environmental, medical, behavioral, or other interventions. These points apply to *prospective* capacity evaluation—with a person whose current and future capacity is in question.

The role is different when the psychologist is performing a *retrospective* evaluation of capacity. These questions concern an opinion of whether the psychologist thinks the person may have had capacity to enter into a contract or some other task in the past.

Undue Influence

Complicating the understanding of capacity is the concept of "undue influence," the focus of chapter 7. Undue influence is a legal concept that refers to a dynamic between an individual and another person. It describes the intentional use of social influence, deception, and manipulation to gain control of the decision making of another. For psychologists, undue influence can be understood as a dynamic of a relationship when a person uses a role and power to exploit the trust, dependency, and fear of another. The role and power permits the person to gain control over the decision making of the victim. In cases of undue influence, a person may have full capacity. Alternatively, there may be cognitive impairment that increases susceptibility and dependence. In the case of Mr. Olsen, although the psychologist is to evaluate capacity, it will be useful to remain mindful of potential issues of elder abuse and neglect, "self-neglect," and undue influence as the psychologist investigates the social circumstances surrounding the referral.

The next chapters will discuss legal standards for various capacities and present a general framework for capacity assessment. In Chapter 6 specific capacity domains will be discussed in detail. Remaining chapters deal with undue influence, working with legal professionals and the court, and emerging issues.

II. Legal Standards of Diminished Capacity

This chapter describes legal approaches to defining diminished capacity and incapacity. Read in tandem with the next chapter on the psychological frameworks for capacity assessment, the explanation highlights the similarities and contrasts between the two approaches to capacity.

Historically, the law's approach to incapacity reflects a long-standing paradox. On the one hand, our legal system has always recognized the situation-specific nature of capacity, depending on the particular event or transaction—such as capacity to make a will, marry, enter into a contract, vote, drive a car, stand trial in a criminal prosecution, and so on (Parry, 1985). A finding of incapacity in any of these matters could nullify or prevent a particular legal act.

On the other hand, at least until very recently, determinations of incapacity in the context of guardianship or conservatorship proceedings were routinely quite global, absolute determinations of one's ability to manage property and personal affairs. A finding of incapacity under guardianship law traditionally justified intrusive curtailments of personal autonomy and resulted in a virtually complete loss of civil rights (Frolik, 1981; Horstman, 1975).

In the last few decades, most states have moved away from the all or nothing approach to guardianship and moved toward a preference for—or at least recognition of—a limited guardianship model that appoints a guardian for the person with incapacity only in those areas of functioning in which capacity is shown to be lacking. One result of this more finely tuned approach to capacity assessment is a fundamental change in terminology in the law.

Historically, it was common to use the term "incompetency" to refer to the legal finding of incapacity, and the term "incapacity" to refer to the clinical finding. That distinction no longer works, as most states have moved away from the terminology of "incompetency" in favor of function-specific "capacity" and "incapacity." Therefore, to avoid confusing the legal and clinical concepts of capacity, we articulate the distinction very simply as either "legal capacity" or "clinical capacity."

> **Starting Point:** Consider state legal standards for the specific transaction at hand. The definition of diminished capacity will depend on the type of transaction or decision under consideration and the particular legal standard of capacity used in the state.

Standards of Capacity for Specific Legal Transactions

The starting point in the law is a presumption that adults possess the capacity to undertake any legal task they choose, unless they have been adjudicated as incapacitated to perform the task in the context of guardianship or conservatorship, or where a party challenging their capacity puts forward sufficient evidence of incapacity in a legal proceeding to meet a requisite burden of proof. The definition of "diminished capacity" in everyday legal practice depends on the type of transaction or decision under consideration, as well as upon the jurisdiction in which one is located (Walsh, 1994; Parry & Gilliam, 2002). Across jurisdictions, legal capacity has multiple definitions, set out in either state statutory and/or case law.

Examples of common transaction-specific legal standards follow. Chapter 6 provides a detailed review of the capacity domains relevant to many of these legal standards.

> For definitions of legal terms common in civil capacity see **Appendix A.**

Testamentary Capacity

By far the most frequently litigated form of capacity—the capacity to make a will—is typically found to be present if the person making the will—a testator—at the time of executing a will, has the capacity to: (1) know the natural objects of his or her bounty (or one's "generosity"); (2) to understand the nature and extent of his or her property; and (3) to interrelate these elements sufficiently to make a disposition of property; (4) by means of a testamentary instrument. (Mezzullo & Woolpert, 2004; Parry et al., 2002; Walsh, 1994). The terminology that the testator must be of "sound mind" is still commonly used.

The legal "test" for testamentary capacity does not require that the person be capable of managing all of his or her affairs or making day-to-day business transactions. Nor must the testator have capacity consistently over time. Capacity is required on the day the will was executed. Thus, a testator may lack testamentary capacity before and/or after executing a will, but if it is made during a "lucid interval," the will remains valid (Parry et al., 2002). Finally, even a

testator who generally possesses the elements of testamentary capacity may have that capacity negated by an "insane delusion" (i.e., irrational perceptions of particular person or events") if the delusion materially affects the will.

Donative Capacity

The law addresses a number of specific capacities related to finances. Capacity to make a gift has been defined by courts to require an understanding of the nature and purpose of the gift, an understanding of the nature and extent of property to be given, a knowledge of the natural objects of the donor's bounty, and an understanding of the nature and effect of the gift. Some states use a higher standard for donative capacity than for testamentary capacity, requiring that the donor know the gift to be irrevocable and that it would result in a

---

A Legal Primer

American law is broadly divided into four areas:

- *Constitutional law* sets the basic framework for governmental powers, civil rights, and civil liberties.
- *Statutes* are enacted by elected legislatures, and set out provisions that may be quite broad in scope or fairly detailed.
- *Administrative rules*, regulations, and policies, interpret and flesh out the statutes.
- *Case law* is the body of principles and rules arising from specific disputes heard in the courts. Judges apply constitutional, statutory, and administrative law to individual conflicts, as well as the principles derived from previous cases, to resolve cases and controversies.

Court decisions provide guidance in interpreting and applying existing law to the real world, while sometimes creating new law. The aggregate of reported cases on a particular subject form a body of jurisprudence referred to as *common law* doctrine. According to the principle of *stare decisis*, courts adhere to decided cases or precedent unless the court finds a compelling reason to overrule it, thus creating new precedent.

When lawyers and judges use the term "legal standard" for capacity, they mean the definition or test of capacity as it exists in statutory law as interpreted by any existing administrative guidelines and case law. For instance, a statutory definition of testamentary capacity may be clarified by will contests in court. A definition of incapacity in guardianship law may be translated into practical terms by a court s evaluation form.

Statutes are written at the local, state, and federal levels. For most capacities in this book, and for adult guardianship, the relevant laws are at the state level. State courts that address matters of civil capacity or guardianship may be specialized family or probate courts, or they may be courts of general jurisdiction in which a judge may be less familiar with the particular issues at stake.

reduction in the donor's assets or estate (Mezzullo et al., 2004; Walsh, 1994). The rationale for the higher standard is that the gift takes effect in the present and not after the death of the donor, so its consequences are potentially greater.

The following capacities are discussed in greater detail in Chapter 6
- Medical consent
- Sexual consent
- Financial
- Testamentary
- Driving
- Independent living

Contractual Capacity

In determining an individual's capacity to execute a contract, courts generally assess the party's ability to understand the nature and effect of the act and the business being transacted (Mezzullo et al., 2004; Walsh, 1994). Accordingly, if the act or business being transacted is highly complicated, a higher level of understanding may be needed to understand its nature and effect, in contrast to a very simple contractual arrangement.

Capacity to Convey Real Property

To execute a deed, a grantor typically must be able to understand the nature and effect of the act at the time of the conveyance (i.e., transfer of title) (Mezzullo & Woolpert, 2004).

Capacity to Execute a Durable Power of Attorney

The standard of capacity for creating a power of attorney has traditionally been based on the capacity to contract. However, some courts have also held that the standard is similar to that for making a will (Regan & Gilfix, 2003). Given the dramatic rise in the use of powers of attorney for purposes of planning for incapacity and their potential for financial abuse, it would not be surprising to see an increase in litigation over capacity to execute a durable power of

attorney and an attempt by courts to articulate the test for capacity with greater detail.

An instructive contrasting approach is offered by an Australian Office of the Public Guardian, which instructs in its educational materials that when making a general durable power of attorney (called an enduring power of attorney in Australia), the person must:

1. know the nature and extent of his or her estate and finances;
2. understand that the power gives the agent complete authority to deal with his or her estate and finances in the same way that he or she can personally do now;
3. know that in a power of attorney, he or she may direct someone else (the agent) to act in a particular way and that the authority can be revoked at any time whilst he or she has capacity;
4. understand that the authority is activated without any formal procedure when he or she loses capacity;
5. appreciate the very high level of trust he or she is placing on the person appointed as agent and understand that the agent is not monitored in any way. If the agent is failing in his or her responsibilities, this is usually only dealt with after the fact in a judicial proceeding (Office of the Public Advocate, 2003).

Capacity to Consent to Medical Care

Capacity to make a health care decision is defined by statute in most states under their advance directive laws. Typical of these legal definitions is the following from the Uniform Health Care Decisions Act:

> "Capacity" means an individual's ability to understand the significant benefits, risks, and alternatives to proposed health care and to make and communicate a health-care decision (Uniform Health-Care Decisions Act of 1993, 1994).

Decisional capacity in health care is rooted in the concept of *informed consent* (Meisel, 1999; Furrow, Greaney, Johnson, Jost, & Schwartz, 2000). Informed consent requires that one's consent to treatment be competent, voluntary, and informed. The concept is based on the principle that a patient has the right to prevent unauthorized contact with his or her person, and therefore a clinician has a duty to disclose relevant information to the patient so that he or she can make an informed decision about treatment. The lack of informed consent is often an issue in medical malpractice claims. It is important to note that capacity is only one element of the test of informed consent.

Thus, a person may have capacity to make a treatment decision, but the treatment decision lacks informed consent if it was either involuntary or unknowing.

State advance directive laws generally authorize physicians to evaluate and document a patient's decisional capacity for medical treatment for purposes of triggering the authority of a surrogate decision-maker without resort to the courts.

Capacity to Execute a Health Care Advance Directive

An individual's capacity to execute an advance directive for health care is different than the capacity to make specific medical decisions. As with durable powers of attorney for financial matters, the test of capacity to execute a health care power of attorney is generally parallel to that of capacity to contract. And, because adjudication of advance directive capacity issues is almost non-existent, there is little specific guidance beyond the contractual paradigm. Accordingly, the psychological models of capacity discussed in the next chapter help to supplement these legal principles with scientifically grounded road signs.

Capacity to Consent to Sexual Relations

Sexual consent law in most states has developed in the context of criminal prosecutions of individuals who have had sex with someone allegedly incapable of consent due to mental retardation. Older victims of sexual assault who suffer from dementia or other cognitive impairments will pose differing clinical assessment challenges, but the legal principles that have developed in the law are essentially the same.

Generally, the law recognizes three factors that must be analyzed in determining legally sufficient consent: (1) knowledge of the relevant facts relating to the decision to be made; (2) the mental capacity to realize and rationally process the risks and benefits of engaging in sexual activity; and (3) voluntariness, meaning the absence of coercion and the presence of a realistic choice between engaging or refraining from the activity. While the factors are fairly uniform, the extent and means of demonstrating these factors is not at all uniform. State courts show significant variability, especially with respect to definitions of mental capacity.

Most states define "mental capacity" to mean that the person cannot understand the nature of sexual conduct—that is, the person does not know either the physiological aspects of sex or the possible consequences of sexual activity, such as pregnancy and the contraction of sexually transmitted diseases. Some states require an added element of appreciating the moral dimension of the decision to engage in sexual conduct, although actually following those moral notions is not required. Thus, the individual may need the capacity to appraise the nature of the possible social stigma or taboo associated with sexual intercourse outside of marriage.

Regardless of the legal standard, an even greater challenge is the lack of a clear standard for the assessment process, i.e., the evaluative criteria and tools to be used in the assessment of capacity to consent to sexual relations.

Capacity to Drive

Capacity to drive a motor vehicle and grounds for revoking the privilege are established by state motor vehicle laws. While variations in the law are common, the Uniform Vehicle Code provides a fairly representative norm. It provides that no license shall be issued when the commissioner has good cause to believe that a person "by reason of physical or mental disability would not be able to operate a motor vehicle with safety upon the highways."

The tremendous variety of physical, mental, and emotional impairments that can result in an inability to operate a motor vehicle safely results in substantial assessment variability, but regardless of the nature or source of impairment, the legal standard ultimately looks at its practical impact on the individual's ability to operate a motor vehicle with reasonable and ordinary control.

Capacity to Mediate

Mediation is increasingly being used as a means of dispute resolution in a broad range of issues that might otherwise go to court. With respect to the capacity needed to engage in mediation, the *ADA Mediation Guidelines* name several factors to be considered by mediators:

> The mediator should ascertain that a party understands the nature of the mediation process, who the parties are, the role of the mediator, the parties' relationship to the mediator, and the issues at hand. The mediator should determine whether the party can assess options and make and keep an agreement (Wood, 2001).

Other Legal Capacities

A host of other legal acts have specific definitions of capacity articulated and honed by statutes and courts in different jurisdictions. For instance, lawyers may wrestle with client capacity to marry, to stand trial, to sue and be sued, or to vote.

Diminished Capacity in State Guardianship Law

State guardianship and conservatorship laws rely on broader and more encompassing definitions of incapacity, a finding of which permits the state to override an individual's right to make his or her own decisions and to appoint someone (a guardian or conservator) to act as the person's surrogate decision-maker for some or all of the person's affairs. The criteria for a finding of incapacity differ among the states, but in all states, the law starts with the presumption of capacity. The burden of proof is on the party bringing the petition to establish sufficient diminished capacity to justify the appointment of a guardian or conservator.

The law of guardianship has evolved extensively from its English roots. Originally,

the law required a finding that the alleged incapacitated person's status was that of an "idiot," "lunatic," "person of unsound mind," or "spendthrift." Present day notions of incapacity instead use a combination of more finely-tuned medical and functional criteria. A common post-World War II paradigm for the definition of incapacity under guardianship laws was a two-pronged test that required: (1) a finding of a disabling condition, such as "mental illness," "mental disability," "mental retardation," "mental condition," "mental infirmity," or "mental deficiency;" and (2) a finding that such condition causes an inability to adequately manage one's personal or financial affairs (Sabatino & Basinger, 2000). Under this definition, the disabling condition prong of the test was quite broad. Many states included "physical illness" or "physical disability" as a sufficient disabling condition, and some opened a very wide door by including "advanced age" and the catch-all "or other cause."

Such amorphous and discriminatory labels invited overly subjective and arbitrary judicial determinations. Over time, states sought to refine both prongs of this test to make the determination of incapacity less label-driven, more specific, and more focused on how an individual functions in society (American Bar Association Commission on the Mentally Disabled and Commission on Legal Problems of the Elderly, 1989; Anderer, 1990). For example, many states have narrowed the qualifying disabling conditions or eliminated them as a criteria altogether on the rationale that diagnosis does not equal disability. Likewise, the second prong of the test—inability to manage one's

---

State Guardianship Laws Mix n Match Four Varying Tests of Incapacity:

- Disabling condition
- Functional behavior (focusing on essential needs)
- Cognitive functioning
- Necessity element or least restrictive alternative criteria

affairs—has been honed by many states to focus only on the ability to provide for one's "essential needs," such as "inability to meet personal needs for medical care, nutrition, clothing, shelter, or safety" (Idaho Code, 1999; Minnesota Statues Annotated, 1998, New Hampshire Revised Statues Annotated, 1999).

In more recent years, "cognitive functioning" tests have gained prominence in many states to supplement or replace one or both prongs of the traditional test. For example, in the 1997 Uniform Guardianship and Protective Proceedings Act, a cognitive functioning test replaces the disabling condition language in the definition of incapacity:

> "Incapacitated person" means an individual who, for reasons other than being a minor, is *unable to receive and evaluate information or make or communicate decisions to such an extent* that the individual lacks the ability to meet essential requirements for physical health, safety, or self-care, even with appropriate technological assistance (Uniform Guardianship and Protective Proceedings Act, 1997).

The three tests—disabling condition, functional behavior, and cognitive functioning—have been "mixed and matched" by states in a variety of ways (Sabatino et al., 2000). Some combine all three (Hurme & Wood, 2006). More importantly, the majority of states have added significant additional requirements as thresholds for guardianship intervention—most commonly a finding that the guardianship is "necessary" to provide for the essential needs of the individual (i.e., there are no other feasible options) or, stated alternatively, that the imposition of a guardianship is "the least restrictive alternative" (Sabatino et al., 2000).

In addition to defining the elements of diminished capacity for purposes of guardianship, most state laws have finally recognized that capacity is not always an all or nothing phenomenon, and have enacted language giving preference to "limited guardianship" in which the guardian is assigned only those duties and powers that the individual is incapable of exercising. Thus, judges, as well as lawyers who draft proposed court orders, need to understand and identify those specific areas in which the person cannot function and requires assistance. Under the principle of the least restrictive alternative, the objective is to leave as much in the hands of the individual as possible.

Undue Influence

Capacity assessment focuses on an individual's cognitive, functional, and decisional abilities relative to the complexity and risk of the legal transaction at hand. Undue influence refers to a dynamic between an individual and another person. It describes the bending of one person's will to the extent that the will of the perpetrator is substituted for that of the victim.

Chapter 7 provides more detail about undue influence with a case example.

Related to legal doctrines of fraud and duress, undue influence may be alleged in legal transactions, such as executing a will, entering a contract, or conveying property to another, as well as in cases of financial abuse, sexual abuse, and even homicide. However, most typically, financial exploitation is the driving force. While diminished capacity may make one more vulnerable to undue influence, it is not a necessary component of the dynamic. Therefore, undue influence can be present even when the victim clearly possesses mental capacity.

Guidance for Lawyers and Judges

Although lawyers seldom receive formal training in capacity assessment, they make capacity judgments on a regular basis whether they realize it or not. It is useful for psychologists and other health professionals to know something about the role lawyers and judges play with respect to capacity determinations.

The decision to provide any legal service to a client contains within it the implicit determination that the client has the capacity to hire the lawyer and to complete the particular legal transaction. In most cases, it is not a difficult determination because there is no doubt about legal capacity. Yet, as society ages, the incidence of cases in which capacity is an issue continues to increase substantially.

One source of guidance for lawyers has been the ABA's *Model Rules of Professional Conduct* (MRPC). Revised in 2002, the *Model Rules* acknowledge capacity assessment challenges, and indeed, suggest a duty to make informal capacity judgments in certain cases. Not all states have adopted the *Model Rules*, but even taking into account state variations, there is a great deal of similarity in direction among the state legal ethics rules. Model Rule 1.14: *Clients with Diminished Capacity*, is most directly on point. It recognizes, first, the goal of maintaining a normal client-lawyer relationship even in the face of diminished capacity; second, the lawyer's discretion to take protective action in the face of diminished capacity; and third, the discretion to reveal confidential information to the limited extent necessary to protect the client's interests.

Part (b) of Rule 1.14 requires three criteria to be met before the lawyer takes protective action:

- the existence of diminished capacity;
- a risk of substantial harm; and
- an inability to act adequately in one's own interest.

Lawyers are familiar with assessing risk and identifying what is in one's interest, but usually they are neither familiar with nor trained in evaluating diminished capacity. Even though taking protective action is permissive ("may") and not mandatory, inaction due to uncertainty puts the lawyer uncomfortably between an ethical rock and a hard place.

The Comment to new Rule 1.14 for the first time gives some guidance in assessing capacity, although the rule itself does not define capacity:

In determining the extent of the client's diminished capacity, the lawyer should consider and balance such factors as: the client's ability to articulate reasoning leading to a decision; variability of state of mind and ability to appreciate consequences of a decision; the

substantive fairness of a decision; and the consistency of a decision with the known long-term commitments and values of the client. In appropriate circumstances, the lawyer may seek guidance from an appropriate diagnostician. (Comment 6 to MRPC 1.14, American Bar Association, 2002).

These qualitative factors blend quite naturally with the normal client interview and the counseling conversation. However, the *Model Rules* do not provide any conceptual, clinical, or practical explanation for the factors (National Conference on Ethical Issues in Representing Older Clients, 1994; Margulies, 1994). To fill in the picture for lawyers and provide a more systematic approach to the capacity assessment process, the ABA Commission on Law and Aging and the APA produced a handbook for lawyers, entitled *Assessment of Older Adults with Diminished Capacity: A Handbook for Lawyers* (2005). The handbook does not lure lawyers into the task of clinical assessment. Rather, it lays out a systematic role for lawyers in capacity screening at three levels:

1. "preliminary screening" of capacity, the goal of which is merely to identify capacity "red flags" and to make a decision whether clinical consultation or referral is advisable;
2. using effective professional consultation or referral effectively for formal assessment, if needed; and
3. making the legal judgment that the level of capacity is either sufficient or insufficient to proceed with representation as requested.

Regardless of whether a clinical assessment is utilized, the final responsibility rests on the shoulders of the attorney to decide whether representation can proceed as requested or not, or whether in appropriate cases, protective action under MRPC Rule 1.14(b) is merited.

In the context of guardianship proceedings, most judges likewise lack a clinical background and are challenged by the demanding role of making legal determinations about an individual's capacity—particularly because evidence may be murky or insufficient—yet fundamental rights hang in the balance. The ABA Commission on Law and Aging and the APA, with the National College of Probate Judges (NCPJ), created a capacity handbook specially designed for judges in these kinds of cases, *Judicial Determination of Capacity of Older Adults in Guardianship Proceedings* (2006).

As with the lawyers' handbook, the judges' version does not propose to arm judges with some kind of capacity test. Rather, it seeks to provide a conceptual framework of capacity, focusing on six areas (or "pillars of capacity") in which information should be collected and examined: (1) medical condition; (2) cognition; (3) everyday functioning; (4) values and preferences; (5) the risk of harm and level of supervision needed; and (6) opportunities to enhance capacity. These elements are amplified in the next chapter and framed within the context of the applicable legal standard for the capacity in question and clinical judgment. The handbook also provides judges with several practical tools: suggestions for communication between judges and clinicians; strategies to enhance the autonomy of the alleged incapacitated person; help in identifying less restrictive alternatives to full guardianship; information about reversible causes of impairment

---

Chapter 8 further discusses working with lawyers and the courts

---

In working with lawyers or judges, it is worthwhile for clinicians to learn whether they are familiar with the above or similar resources, because it can improve the quality and efficiency of communication and collaboration between the two disciplines.

Some Comparisons Between the Legal and Clinical Models

As a bridge between the legal standards discussed above and the conceptual framework for clinicians in the next chapter, it is worth noting three characteristics that put certain similarities and differences between legal and clinical approaches to capacity in relief.

Transactions or Domains

One is that the focus on particular "transactions" in the law is parallel in many respects to what psychologists would characterize as functional "domains," although clinical domains are much more finely articulated.

Binary versus Continuous

Two, the law tends to ask about capacity for specific transactions in a binary fashion—i.e., is capacity present or lacking—somewhat like an on/off switch. Clinicians are more oriented toward understanding capacities as variable continuums in which there may be no bright line between the presence or absence of capacity. While the law is warming up to the variable continuum notion, the transactional focus of the legal question still pushes for a binary yes or no answer.

Conceptual versus Operational

Third, legal definitions of transactional capacity tend to follow a fairly simple conceptual template: can the individual understand the nature and effect of (fill in the task) and perform whatever the essential function is necessary to implement the task. Thus, they tend to articulate tests that are sound in principle but not necessarily helpful in parsing the operational cognitive, behavioral, or emotional abilities necessary to meet the standard. Clinical assessment fills in that detail but must be clearly linked to the relevant legal standard.

III. Conceptual Framework for Capacity Assessment

Psychologists bring several strengths to the capacity assessment process, most notably but not exclusively, skills in the use of standardized assessment. The use of standardized assessment is important because capacity assessments have been criticized for being vague and subjective. Comprehensive evaluation that incorporates objective data is especially important in complex cases. For some older adults there may be subtle deficits in some areas and not others, a strong desire on the part of the individual to retain personal autonomy, significant risks in the decisional outcomes, family conflict, team disagreements, variable clinical status, undue influence, and so forth. When assessing broad capacities with cognitive and procedural components, such as "the capacity to live independently," the task can be rather overwhelming. It is not uncommon to feel confused at times by the capacity assessment task.

A clinical judgment about capacity of an older adult is exactly that—a professional clinical decision. There is no equation, cookbook, or test battery for the assessment of capacity. A one-size fits all approach is doomed to failure because of the varying domains of capacity, legal standards used to define specific capacities, and the need to integrate multiple sources of data in complex clinical situations. It is, however, useful to have a framework of the critical elements in capacity assessment, which may function to guide the psychologist in the assessment process.

This handbook will be based upon a nine-part framework for capacity assessment. The framework represents an expansion of psychologist Tom Grisso's pioneering model for legal capacity (1986) that included six elements: causal, functional, contextual, interactive, judgmental, and dispositional. The nine-part framework used in this book expands on this model in the context of clinical assessment of older adults and the application of capacity standards in state guardianship law.

> **A Framework for Capacity Assessment**
>
> 1. Legal Standard
> 2. Functional Elements
> 3. Diagnosis
> 4. Cognitive Underpinnings
> 5. Psychiatric or Emotional Factors
> 6. Values
> 7. Risk Considerations
> 8. Steps to Enhance Capacity
> 9. Clinical Judgment of Capacity

This framework will be applied in a step by step description of capacity assessment in Chapter 5, and will be followed in each of the case examples provided for various specific capacities in Chapter 6.

Similarities with Psychological Assessment

Inherent in this framework are many elements of any comprehensive psychodiagnostic and/or neuropsychological assessment, such as a determination of the neurocognitive or neuropsychiatric diagnosis, definition of the cognitive strengths and weakness, functioning in the environment, description of the individual's preferences and background, and recommendations for treatment. Some elements are unique to capacity assessment—namely the consideration of the legal standard for the capacity in question, a risk analysis, and a professional clinical judgment about decision-making capacity.

Development of the Framework

Readers may recognize elements of the framework in this handbook from the ABA-APA-NCPJ Judges' Handbook concerning capacity in guardianship. The framework was expanded in this handbook for use by clinicians to organize assessments for a variety of specific capacities. The conceptual framework, illustrated in the scales figure below, was developed by reviewing theoretical and legal models for capacity as broadly conceived. First, we considered Grisso's (1986) model of legal capacity, as well as a similar model in a VA (1997) practice guideline for capacity assessment by psychologists. Second, we reviewed various legal frameworks for capacity under guardianship, including state-by-state comparison of legal standards for incapacity in state guardianship law, state-by-state requirements for capacity evaluation in guardianship, and national probate court standards for capacity evaluation.

Components of the Framework

Legal Standard

Clinical evaluations of capacity are grounded in a clinician's opinion about a person's ability to make a decision or perform a task that has a specific definition in the law. Therefore, the legal standard for the capacity in question forms the foundation of a capacity assessment. A finding of incapacity may ultimately result in a person's loss of a legally recognized right to make a decision or perform a task. For example, a clinical finding that a person lacks testamentary capacity—lacks the sufficient knowledge and judgment to "competently" create or alter a will—means the individual's stated choices for that will are not recognized in settlement of the estate. Therefore any assessment regarding a matter of civil capacity requires that the psychologist familiarize him or herself with the legal standard—most often by consulting with an attorney. When working in a medical organization, organizational policies and procedures may further define these legal standards and how they are applied in the healthcare system. For psychologists new to the capacity assessment task, legal standards may be confusing. The language in legal standards may not be consistent with clinical concepts, and may be so vague as to not provide much clarification for the clinical task. To locate legal standards, a psychologist may consult statutory and case law precedent within his or her state. Most likely, the psychologist will then want to consult with an attorney to discuss the legal standard and its meanings from a legal perspective.

> **How do I find legal standards?**
> Discuss with an attorney, such as the referring attorney, hospital counsel, or colleague; see also **Chapter 2.**

For example, a common set of legal standards for medical consent capacity is the ability to understand and appreciate diagnostic and treatment information, reason about the risks and benefits of treatment options, and express a treatment choice. (These standards are further described in Chapter 6, section 1). The statutory or case law will not define exactly what "appreciation" means, and how it should be evaluated, but, if these are the factors in the statutory framework, a clinical evaluation should address each of these. As another example, the Uniform Guardianship and Protective Proceedings Act, a model guardianship statute, (National Conference of Commissioners on Uniform State Laws, 1997) defines an incapacitated individual as someone who is "unable to receive and evaluate information or make or communicate decisions to such an extent that the individual lacks the ability to meet essential requirements for physical health, safety, or self-care, even with appropriate technological assistance." Therefore, the psychologist may want to build a test battery that generally assesses the concepts of receiving and evaluating information, and communicating it, such as neuropsychological tests that assess language, memory, executive functioning, or functional and decisional capacity measures tailored to target these standards.

Functional Elements

Functional assessment is a common component of gerontological assessment, and has been appreciated by clinicians (Scogin & Perry, 1987) who categorize functioning into the activities of daily living (ADLs) (e.g., grooming, toileting, eating, transferring, dressing) and the instrumental activities of daily living (IADLs) (e.g., abilities to manage finances, health, and functioning in the home and community). In the context of capacity assessment, an assessment of "everyday functioning" means some sort of tailored evaluation—with interview questions and, when possible direct assessment and observation of the individual's functioning—on the specific task in question. For example, when evaluating medical consent capacity, a broad assessment of cognition would be followed by a specific assessment of medical decision-making capacity using a consent capacity instrument; when evaluating capacities for financial management, a broad assessment of cognition would be followed by specific assessment of the individual's knowledge, skills, and judgment relative to financial tasks relevant to the person's financial holdings and history, using a financial capacity instrument. Neuropsychological assessment may only assess cognition and may not include specific standardized functional assessment; *therefore one difference between capacity assessment and most neuropsychological assessment is this focus on functioning,* and the inclusion of some method to assess the specific capacity in question using direct assessment.

Diagnoses

Documentation of the medical diagnoses is a key element in capacity determination as they may be the causative factors explaining any functional disability. Grisso refers to the condition producing the disability as the "causal factor" in his model of capacity assessment (Grisso, 2003). With aging, a wide range of neurological and psychiatric conditions may influence capacity—for example, Alzheimer's disease or other forms of dementia, stroke, Parkinson's disease, traumatic brain injury, schizophrenia, bipolar disorder, and more (Dymek, Atchison, Harrell, & Marson, 2001; Kim, Karlawish, & Caine, 2002). Some of these conditions may be temporary and even reversible if treated, including delirium, depression, bipolar disorder, and psychotic disorders, therefore in addition to identifying the cause of the functional problem, it is important to describe the prognosis and possibility of improvement with time or treatment. The identification of the causes of any cognitive or behavioral impairment leads to an understanding of the likely course of the problem, prognosis, and identification of any treatments that may help. Because legal professionals are not clinically trained, it is critical to spell out information on prognosis in plain language—is the condition likely to get better, get worse, or stay the same, and if a change is likely to occur, when might that be?

Cognitive Underpinnings

In Grisso's model the "functional" element encompasses all facets of the individual's thinking and functioning. In our framework for clinical assessment we emphasize three elements of functioning to be separately addressed in clinical evaluation through interview or direct objective measures: cognitive functioning, psychiatric or emotional functioning, and everyday functioning.

Many disorders that affect capacity do so because they have a direct effect on cognitive functioning, including insight and awareness of deficits (e.g., dementia) (Gurrera, Moye, Karel, Azar, & Armesto, 2006; Marson et al., 1996). Some capacities, such as treatment or research consent are essentially cognitive or decisional in nature. Other capacities, such as driving or financial management, while they involve a behavioral component, also rely heavily on underlying cognitive functioning (Moye & Marson, 2007). In terms of guardianship, cognitive functioning is a component of statutory standards for capacity in many states (Sabatino & Basinger, 2000). For example, the aforementioned UGPPA definition of incapacity includes several elements of cognitive functioning. Psychologists' training and background in comprehensive assessment of cognitive domains is highly relevant to the evolving concepts of capacity as being complex and multifactorial, rather than an all-or-none proposition.

Psychiatric or Emotional Factors

Just as the mere presence of a medical or neurological disorder does not necessarily mean capacity is impaired, the presence of a psychiatric or emotional disturbance, such as thought or mood disorder, does not imply diminished capacity. An individual could have symptoms of depression, anxiety, or psychotic disorder and still be quite able to process information. However, when psychiatric or emotional disturbance is significant, such as severe depression, paranoia, or disinhibition, it may limit reasoning and judgment, and therefore impair capacity (Grisso et al., 1995). Many individuals with psychiatric or emotional disturbance may improve with time and treatment, and therefore it is especially critical in the capacity report to recommend treatment interventions and a time frame for reconsidering capacity.

Values and Preferences

A person's race, ethnicity, culture, gender, sexual orientation, and religion may impact his or her values and preferences (Blackhall, Murphy, Frank, Michel, & Azen, 1995; Hornung et al., 1998), and these lay the foundation for decisions. Age, cohort, and life experience are critical in forming values and preferences. Sexual orientation may not only influence values, but may have special implications in surrogate decision making (who is the person's family and who is the person's legally recognized decision maker). Cultural beliefs and practices may inform decisional preferences including the manner in which decisions are made (individual as decision maker versus family). Therefore all of these factors are crucial to consider in capacity assessment.

In this handbook we use the term "values" to refer to an underlying set of beliefs, concerns, and approaches that guide personal decisions, where as we use "preferences" to refer to the preferred option of various choices that is informed by values. For example, a person may value not being a burden on others, so may have a treatment preference that results in less caregiving burden. For ease, we will use the term "values and preferences" to refer to both of these factors.

Even when cognitive functioning may be compromised, for instance by dementia, a person may still be able to express important deep-rooted values underlying their decisions (Karel, Moye, Bank, & Azar, 2007). Further, choices that are linked with lifetime values may be rational for an individual even if outside the norm. For example, a choice to live in what many might consider substandard housing (e.g., a cabin in the woods without running water) may reflect a long-standing preference to live in such housing.

The extent to which an individual's current decisions are consistent with long-standing values may be an indicator of capacity (American Bar Association, 2002) although it should be noted that values may change with experience or may be significantly influenced by family, social network, culture or religion, so a change in values does not indicate a change in capacity. In addition, knowledge of an individual's values helps to inform the plan of care for the patient. It is especially important to be cognizant of an individual's values, and how these may vary from those of the evaluator—*as capacity determinations should be based on the capacity of the individual in question, and not a mismatch in values between the patient and the clinician.* For example, choices to extend life, or to decline life-sustaining treatments, may be at odds with what an evaluator may choose for him or herself in that situation, but reflect the individual patient's values and beliefs. Values considerations are also important in a broad array of financial transactional capacities. Is the choice to transfer assets to another through a contract, home sale, or even marriage consistent with the financial choices (and underlying values which informed those) the person has made in the past?

Risk of Harm and Level of Supervision Needed

Many capacity evaluations are at heart a risk assessment (Ruchinskas, 2005). Thus, the evaluation of the person and his or her medical conditions, cognitive and functional abilities, personal values and preferences, all elements that affect their day to day functioning, must be analyzed in reference to the risk of the situation at hand. Does the specific treatment or research decision involve a high degree of risk? Is the home situation isolated, unsafe, or proximal to risks? Does the legal contract involve a great risk to the individual's assets? Is money transferred in the will to an individual or institution large in the context of total assets? An analysis of risk is not merely a consideration of the condition and its effects, but also takes into account the environmental supports and demands, or what Grisso (2003) terms the "interactive" component. Strong social and environmental supports may decrease the risk while lack of supports may increase it. Thus, it is at this point in the framework that a consideration of the person's social context is made. The level of intervention or supervision recommended as a result of the capacity assessment must match the risk of harm to the individual and the corresponding level of supervision required to mitigate such risk, and must include a full exploration of the least restrictive alternatives (Sabatino & Basinger, 2000). Traditionally, capacity evaluation has been primarily concerned with risks of harm to oneself, and the state's obligation to protect those who are vulnerable. However, serious risks to others (such as occur when unable to drive a motor vehicle safely) may enter into clinical judgments of capacity.

Means to Enhance Capacity

An essential component of a capacity assessment is a consideration of what can be done to maximize the person's functioning. Practical accommodations (such as vision aids, medication reminders) and medical, psychosocial, or educational interventions (such as physical or occupational therapy, counseling, medications or training) may enhance capacity. Many age-related cognitive and sensory declines can be accommodated. If improvement of capacity is possible with treatment for underlying conditions, clinical recommendations may guide the referral source, or if the assessment is part of a court case, may guide the judge in deciding when to re-hear the case. Further, clinical recommendations for intervention may directly inform the individual's plan of care. Like all good psychological assessment, capacity assessment is often an opportunity for intervention. Of course, this would not apply in a retrospective evaluation of capacity in situations where intervention is not an option (e.g., the person is deceased).

Clinical Judgment

As illustrated in the scales figure, the fulcrum of a capacity assessment is the clinical judgment. A capacity assessment is built upon consideration of the legal standard for the capacity in question. The more standardized and structured assessment of the individual's diagnosis, cognitive, psychiatric, and everyday functioning must be balanced with a consideration of the individual's values and preferences, risk considerations, and the possibility for enhancement of the apparent level of capacity through treatments, aids, and enhancements.

The conclusion section of the report describes the findings of the assessment. However, a mere description of the findings is not enough; the psychologist must provide a clear "yes or no" opinion about the capacity in question. In some cases, the judgment is rather obvious. For example, an individual may have advanced dementia with severe impairment across a range of functioning, and, therefore, clearly lack capacity for the issue in question. Or, an individual may have no or minimal impairments in assessed functional abilities and clearly have capacity for the task in question.

However, the most challenging situation is that of individuals whose capacity impairment is not obvious—and these are the cases that psychologists are most likely to be asked to assess. These individuals in the "middle ground" of capacity may have moderate impairments in many areas, or significant impairment in some areas but not others, or, significant impairment, concerns about that are mitigated by consideration of the person's values, preferences, social supports, and risks.

In most situations the psychologist will need to arrive at a "binary" or "dichotomous" answer to the specific capacity question. An inherent tension in arriving at this decision is that in many situations capacity may be operating as more of a continuous variable, yet the psychologist must provide a dichotomous answer, as illustrated in the figure. For many psychologists, this sort of integration of data to arrive at a dichotomous conclusion is a new and uncomfortable role. The task is to consider all the data and offer an opinion as to whether the data, considered in context of values, risks, and enhancements, lean more in favor of or against the person's capacity. In some situations, it may help to further delineate the capacity task—e.g., the person has the capacity to make a simple medical decision but not a complex or high-risk one. There are situations in which the psychologist may believe he or she cannot provide a strict "yes or no" answer, and may say the person has marginal capacity, if this can be supported by the evidence. However, it is important that a finding of "marginal capacity," rather than a yes/no finding, does not represent discomfort with "sticking one's neck out" and offering a clear opinion. More explanation of this process and examples appear in the following chapters.

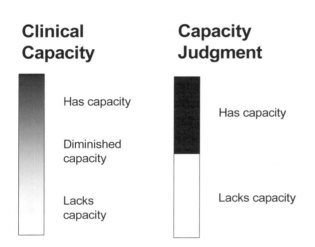

IV. Investigating the Referral and Planning Your Approach

Capacity assessments require more attention on the "pre-assessment" phase to determine what is being assessed and how the assessment should be planned. Therefore, a capacity assessment starts long before the psychologist sits down with the older adult. The goal of this chapter is to help orient psychologists to the key pre-assessment issues involved in an assessment of capacity. Steps in this chapter are outlined in the worksheet following Chapter 5.

Roles Psychologists Play in Capacity Assessments

A large part of the orientation to the capacity assessment process depends on the setting in which the psychologist works and the role played vis à vis the older adult and the system in which the capacity question is arising. Capacity assessments may arise through a wide range of mechanisms. The context of the setting will impact the procedure for the assessment. The context of the case will determine who is the "client" and the capacity in question.

> Refer to **Appendix A**
> for definition of the term client.

Medical Setting

Most hospitals have rules and regulations that address informed consent in situations in which the patient is clearly incapacitated and there is an immediate threat of harm or risk of death to the patient. However, there are other situations of medical consent that are not emergent, and for which a psychologist might be asked to provide an opinion of capacity. Often these arise when a patient is refusing medical treatment; when a patient is agreeing with a doctor's recommendations, the doctor is less likely to evaluate capacity.

For example, in what situations can a person refuse a potentially life saving/sustaining coronary artery bypass graft? What if that individual is psychiatrically stable (at his or her baseline) but has considerable anxiety or paranoia? What if that individual is more acutely psychotic? Can a person with diminished cognitive functioning decide to stop dialysis? What if the decision comes after several days off dialysis in which a delirium is setting in? Can an individual with disorganized reasoning due to micro vascular insults refuse antihypertensive medications or anticoagulation medications that may prevent future infarcts? What if he or she refuses even though he or she also states that it is important to preserve mental capacity?

In these situations, if there is a clinical finding of incapacity by a physician or another professional authorized to determine capacity in the state and in the hospital, it may permit the individual's healthcare proxy, agent under a durable power of attorney for healthcare, and in many states next of kin to consent to the medical procedure. However, even this situation requires some investigation and thinking through. What if a daughter or son is the healthcare proxy and consents to anticoagulation therapy, but is not able to support the patient in monitoring blood levels and adjusting medications? So, part of the investigatory process is to think through the outcomes of a potential yes or no finding on capacity and determine the feasibility of various solutions.

Long-term Care and Rehabilitation Units

A psychologist may offer an opinion to a medical team regarding a patient's capacity to make a medical decision while residing in a long-term care setting. In these settings psychologists are frequently asked to participate in clinical decisions about a person's capacity to live independently, and in some cases to manage finances.

In a rehabilitation or transitional setting, these evaluations are especially key as they significantly impact treatment and discharge planning. Psychologists will need to comment on the course of the illness as an individual's capacity may improve dramatically over a period of time. In some cases, an individual has entered the hospital setting from a less than ideal situation—such as a homeless shelter. The team wants to know if the individual can be discharged back to a homeless shelter in the context of his or her current cognitive functioning. A decision about the capacity to live independently often does not have legal ramifications. However, if a nursing home placement is considered necessary, some facilities require the appointment of a legally authorized decision maker to consent to the placement, prior to admission. Therefore the opinion regarding the capacity to live independently—in order to be discharged home—can evolve to have tremendous implications for the individual's rights if guardianship is sought.

Guardianship Proceedings

In some situations, it is clear from the outset that the reason for the capacity evaluation is to determine the need for a guardian. This may happen in an inpatient or outpatient setting, or in a setting unrelated to medical care. A petition for guardianship requiring a capacity evaluation may be brought by concerned family members, social service agency, or adult protective services. A psychologist's role in this case is to offer information as an expert to be used by the court in making the determination. In some cases, the capacity determination and guardianship order may be contested, meaning that there may be multiple experts involved. Depending upon the state, there may be a form required by the court to document the evaluation and conclusions. In addition, a guardianship case may occasionally require additional oral expert testimony in court. The psychological evaluation for guardianship also has the potential to identify areas of retained functioning, and to therefore recommend domains in which a guardianship order may be limited. This means the individual retains the rights to make decisions in that area. Such statements provide opportunities for the individual to retain rights, as well as a sense of autonomy.

Criminal Proceedings

A psychologist may become involved in evaluating civil capacities but within a criminal setting if a crime against an older adult is involved. In these cases, the psychologist may work with law enforcement as part of the investigational team. These cases may include current or retrospective determination of capacity and may require oral testimony in court. The setting of the capacity evaluation within a criminal proceeding can have tremendous implications for the approach the psychologist takes to confidentiality and consent, as will be further described below. Cases involving "criminal capacities" (e.g., whether an accused older adult has the capacity for criminal responsibility) represents a different area of clinical practice, typically by a psychologist with specialized forensic training, and are not within the scope of this handbook.

Investigator

A psychologist may be hired by an older adult's attorney to provide opinion regarding capacity issues. These consultations may or may not require a report and are considered fact finding for the attorney involved.

Unexpected Case Arising in Clinical Practice

Finally, there may be situations that arise during routine clinical work that result in questions of incapacity. For example, while completing a clinical dementia work-up of a patient, the psychologist learns that he or she has made some very poor recent financial decisions or been victim to financial exploitation. In these cases, the psychologist may raise the issue of diminished capacity, and the evaluation may evolve to become a capacity evaluation (with appropriate consent from the patient). If elder abuse has occurred the psychologist will also report to and involve adult protective services.

Key Questions to Orient Yourself to the Case

What Functional Capacity Is in Question?

Because it is the goal to craft a report that describes the older adult's specific strengths and weaknesses, it is necessary to take time to ascertain exactly what domain is in question.

Answers to this question may include: medical consent, financial abilities, independent living, the ability to engage in binding contracts, the ability to buy or sell property, testamentary capacity, the capacity to drive, and the capacity to consent to sexual activity. Capacity is an evolving clinical and legal concept, so additional domains may be identified in the future.

What Data Are Needed to Answer the Functional Question?

Once the psychologist determines the domain of capacity, it will suggest the type of functional evaluation that may be needed. If the capacity is largely decisional in nature, for example, the ability to engage in a contract, the testing will focus on specific decision-making abilities relevant to contractual capacities and related neurocognitive domains, such as memory, executive function, and reasoning. If the capacity involves performance aspects, such as financial management to include check writing, independent living to include household chores, or driving, the testing will involve direct

---

Getting Oriented to the Case
What: What types of decisional or functional processes are in question?
What data are needed?
Am I an appropriately qualified evaluator?
Who: Who is the client?
What is the older adult s background?
Who is requesting the evaluation?
Who are the interested parties?
Who sees the report?
Is the court or litigants involved?
When: How urgent is the request?
Is there a court date?
What is the time frame of interest?
Is the individual medically stable?
Where: In what context / setting does the evaluation take place?
Why: Why now?
What is the history of the case?
Will a capacity evaluation resolve the problem?

assessment and observation of these performance skills and related neurocognitive functions, such as visual-spatial and executive functions.

Who Is Bringing the Case to Your Attention?

The answer to this question may include health care professionals, attorneys, family members, social service agencies, or adult protective services. As the psychologist asks about the background of the case, insights into the most pressing matters and a list of potential collateral interviewees may be developed.

What Level of Evidence Is Possible?

A related question is to consider the ideal set of data versus the possible, and what this may mean for the assessment outcome. For example, when asked to evaluate capacity to drive, further discussed in Chapter 6, an optimal evaluation may include in-office cognitive testing and on-road driving evaluation. What if the psychologist does not have the ability to refer the older adult to an on-road test? What if financial capacities are questioned but the older adult refuses to participate in a comprehensive assessment of financial abilities, although participates in cognitive evaluation, and there is strong evidence of financial exploitation? What if the psychologist is asked to make a retrospective determination of capacity, but has limited records of cognitive and functional abilities?

In such cases, the psychologist needs to determine if it is permissible to offer an opinion about capacity with a less than ideal level of evidence, in the context of the risks and benefits to the older adult and others of not offering an opinion. In these situations, the psychologist should clearly indicate in the report any limitations in the data that might exist.

What Is the History of the Problem?

Usually, when a request for a capacity evaluation is made, regardless of setting, some crisis has arisen. It can be helpful to step back and inquire about the older adult's previous level of functioning and the history of the complaint. For example in medical settings, has there been a history of poor or marginal compliance that has now become a more serious risk? In financial domains, has the older adult had a history of poor or eccentric financial management, but now may be exploited by fraud? In terms of independent living, does the older adult have a history with social services regarding difficulties with home management? Is there a history of interpersonal difficulties? These data can provide context that will help the psychologist design the most appropriate assessment and plan.

The psychologist will want to be particularly attentive to the history of high-risk behaviors. A referring party may be alarmed about the potential for a high-risk behavior. The psychologist will want to consider how serious is the risk and how likely, given the history of behaviors relevant to the capacity question. For example, is the referring party simply worried about the person "leaving the stove on," but there has been no effort to intervene (e.g., disable the stove); or has the person left the stove on despite efforts to disable the stove and there is evidence of fires or serious burns. Obviously, the psychologist also will want to know if any high-risk behaviors are quite new to the person or have occurred over time, as these may also point to an acute cause of confusion that could be reversible.

Are the Courts Already Involved and/ or Will They Be Involved in the Future?

Cases that arise in medical centers may involve determining if an individual has the ability to consent to treatment. In these cases you will be providing clinical data to assist the treatment providers. The report may never end up in court.

However, if a psychologist is being brought in to assist with a guardianship proceeding for example, it could be prior to court involvement or after courts are already involved. In the former case, the referral may be in an information gathering phase, trying to determine if it is even necessary to pursue a guardianship. If the court is currently involved, determine what action is pending and ask for all relevant court records to review on the case. If a court is currently involved it is helpful to know the timetable for the evaluation and report.

If Litigation Is Involved, Is It a Civil Matter or Criminal Matter?

The vast majority of capacity cases come about through the probate court concerning matters of guardianship and estate. Cases involving fraud or elder abuse may become criminal prosecution of the perpetrator. Therefore, the capacity may still concern a "civil" issue, such as capacity to enter a contract, but the context for the case is criminal. The criminal context may bring to bear different relevant standards. For example, the level of proof may be "beyond a reasonable doubt" in criminal matters.

What Is the Time Frame of Interest?

A psychologist may be asked to make a retrospective evaluation of capacity—given the data available, did the person have the capacity to change a will? Or, a psychologist may be asked to evaluate the person's capacity in the here and now. At times, a psychologist may also be asked to project capacity into the future— given what is known about the diagnostic cause of diminished capacity, would capacity get better, worse, or stay the same.

Who Are the Interested Parties or "Players" Involved in the Case?

No matter what the context, there can be widely varying opinions and motivations surrounding the older adult's capacity. Be familiar with all of those with potential interest in the case and try to assess the motivations of the different participants. That may include family members, attorneys, other experts, physicians, and social workers. For example, in a case of contested capacity involving an alleged incapacitated person, there may be multiple adult children involved, perhaps children from multiple marriages, their attorneys and experts, plus social services all with differing opinions and motivations.

The court may very well include other witnesses when making its determinations regarding capacity. These witnesses may include other experts, law enforcement, and others. The psychologist needs to be aware that the clinical evidence that they provide may only be part of the total evidence involved in the case. In other situations, the psychological report may be the only data upon which a legal determination of capacity is made (e.g., most "routine" guardianship hearings).

Will Answering the Question About Capacity Resolve the Problem?

Sometimes thorny clinical problems are initially posed as capacity issues, but the core issue, such as a family systems issue, may not be resolved with such an assessment. For example, nursing home staff may ask a psychologist to comment upon the capacity of someone who is refusing personal care. Although indeed the person may be so impaired as to be unable to understand the consequences of refusing care (e.g., bathing), a finding of incapacity will not solve the problem. The staff needs to determine how to deliver the care to the resistant patient. Similarly, nursing home staff may have unrealistic ideas about what a guardian can offer. A guardian can provide key decisional input but cannot monitor a person and compel behavior from minute to minute.

Are There Less Restrictive Alternatives That Might Resolve the Problem Without a Capacity Evaluation?

Ideally, the clinician will work to put into place the least restrictive alternative that provides the older adult protection (if needed). The older adult may have some mechanisms in place that provide decisional support. These mechanisms can include the use of advance directives, healthcare proxy, a durable power of attorney for finances and/or healthcare, or a representative payee. For some of these mechanisms, a capacity evaluation may still be required, but with others, there may be a solution that does not require going to that length. With a highly functional family system and some input from the older adult regarding their wishes, it can be possible to avoid an adversarial approach.

What Is the Urgency of the Request— Is an Answer Needed Now?

Some capacity evaluation requests are very urgent. For example, a person with diminished cognitive abilities may be insisting on leaving "against medical advice" (AMA) discharge immediately, and the staff is unsure if the person has the capacity to leave AMA or must be prevented from going in some manner. In any situation the psychologist will want to determine if the individual is medically and psychiatrically stable. In other situations, the psychologist may determine the person is not stable, and the capacity question can wait. For example, the person will not come to harm if treatment is delayed for a period of time. This will allow the psychologist to work with the team to offer interventions to maximize the individual's cognitive functioning prior to the capacity assessment.

What Is the Older Adult's Cultural Background, Language Needs, and Sensory Functioning?

As with any psychological assessment, the psychologist will want to consider what adaptations may need to be made in approaching the older adult to maximize understanding. Obviously, if the individual is a non-english speaker, the evaluation must be done in the individual's language, using a translator if necessary. Attention must then be paid to issues of translation of measures and also of test bias. Cultural factors influence more than the method of assessment, but may also influence the context in which the capacity question arose. For example, if an older adult is refusing a medical treatment, was the older adult provided with sufficient information, and did he or she understand it? Was there freedom to make a decision that was informed and voluntary? Did issues such as immigrant status, economical status, culturally informed perceptions of illness and the role of medical treatment influence the older adult's decision making? How does the older adult wish for his or her family to be involved in decisions?

In addition to cultural and language concerns, potential sensory difficulties need to be accommodated so that the older adult can see and hear relevant information during the evaluation. In addition, it may be useful to schedule shorter testing periods, and if more lengthy testing is required, to do so over several days.

To accommodate sensory loss, address:
Background noise
Seating position
Lighting
Large print materials
Hearing and visual aids
Speaking style and pace
Duration of testing sessions
See *APA Guidelines for Psychological Practice with Older Adults* for more details at www.apa.org/practice/adult.pdf

Am I Appropriately Qualified to Do the Capacity Assessment?

At this point, the psychologist has amassed a lot of information about what data are needed to answer the capacity question and any mitigating contextual factors. Next, the psychologist must consider if he or she has the qualifications to do the assessment (e.g., professional competencies in the assessment of older adults). Further qualifications may arise depending upon the particulars of the case. For example, is a bilingual psychologist needed? Will the questions be better answered by an occupational therapist? Is the situation so medically complex that the capacity question may be better answered by or in conjunction with a medical doctor? Is the older adult's underlying condition one in which the psychologist has experience assessing—different skills may be needed to assess an individual with serious mental illness, versus dementia or developmental disability.

Do I Have a Conflict of Interest?

If there is a conflict of interest between the psychologist and patient, it should be identified, and where appropriate, disclosed and/or resolved. For instance, it is not advisable to do a capacity assessment with an older adult known through a therapeutic, personal, or professional relationship because it would create a dual relationship as described in the *Ethical Principles of Psychologists and Code of Conduct* (American Psychological Association, 2002).

Reviewing the Records

A thorough clinical assessment includes a review of available medical records. However, obtaining medical, legal, and other records becomes even more important in capacity assessments. The medical records are needed to address the presence and type of medical condition producing functional disability, current medication regimens, the course of the illness, and medical risk factors for cognitive impairment. For example, a psychologist may be able to obtain previous cognitive testing to use as a baseline, neuroimaging information, a description of the clinical course, information regarding the use of assistive technologies, etc.

In guardianship cases, there may be conflicting expert opinions regarding the need for a guardian. Accessing previous assessments and legal records can help the clinician to organize the current assessment. In other types of capacity cases, for example those regarding financial capacity, it can be helpful to access banking statements and other financial information to determine if the older adult's report is accurate. For example, the older adult states that they always pay their bills on time, but there is objective evidence to the contrary. Or the older adult confidently states monthly income of $1,200 but records contradict that information. Family members, social workers, or private attorneys can be helpful in obtaining such records.

Obtaining Informed Consent

Review the purpose of the evaluation, the nature of the evaluation, and the evaluation procedures with the older adult. Define the risks for the person being assessed that include a loss of decision-making rights, potential lack of confidentiality, and the possible need for a guardian or conservator. Also discuss any possible benefits to the procedure that may include the gathering of helpful clinical information that can be used in treatment planning or as evidence in criminal matters on the person's behalf. Include a description of the risks of not consenting. For example, in some situations the psychologist may be responding to a request to complete a court document regarding the need for a guardian, and may need to complete that regardless of whether or not the person consents to a full evaluation. Therefore, the psychologist might explain that the risks of consenting include the loss of rights associated with guardianship; the risks of refusing is that the psychologist will be required to complete the documentation without having obtained full input from the patient.

After disclosing information—if necessary in small "chunks" and with written support—ask the older adult to state back the purpose of the interview and risks and benefits involved. This process may take several attempts and require breaking the information down into simpler pieces. The goal is to maximize understanding.

The consent process must consider who is the client and who will see the report. For example, in a court-ordered case, the report will be used as evidence and viewed by all parties to the case. In some states these capacity declarations become public documents. It is the psychologist's job to ascertain who is the client in each specific case and to ask the referring person who will see the report. In situations where the person being assessed is not the psychologist's "client," informed consent procedures must be modified to explain the limits of confidentiality to the person being assessed.

In the report, document the informed consent process in detail, including how the assessment was described to the individual, the risks and benefits disclosed, and the extent of the person's understanding.

Of course an obvious question is whether the individual for whom you are evaluating capacity has the capacity to consent to the assessment. In some cases the level of ability needed to consent to the assessment is lower or different than the ability being assessed. For example, you may be evaluating the person's ability to manage a complex financial estate that requires a higher level of understanding than making a decision about whether to consent to the capacity assessment process. Several outcomes are possible, as summarized in the table below.

Capacity Evaluation Consent Outcomes			
		Agreement to Evaluation	
Capacity to Consent		Yes	No
	Yes	Valid Agreement	Valid Refusal
	No	Incapable Agreement or Assent	Incapable Refusal

The person may have capacity to consent to the evaluation, and either agrees or refuses. In this case, the person has provided a valid agreement or refusal, and this can be documented. Alternatively the person may not have the capacity to consent to the evaluation, and either agrees or refuses. If the person agrees, he or she is generally said to have "assented" and the assessment process goes forward. If the person disagrees, and refuses to comply with an interview, then the psychologist must document why the person is believed to lack the capacity to refuse the evaluation. In some situations, the capacity evaluation stops there. In other situations, where a capacity evaluation is court ordered, the psychologist may be asked to provide an opinion based on his or her observations of the person.

> Refer to **Chapter 8**
> for a discussion of third party observers

Billing

Because capacity assessments can arise in diverse settings, mechanisms for billing vary as well. In settings where the primary goal of the assessment is related to medical care, the assessment may be billed to Medicare or private insurance. However, when the referral is clearly forensic in nature from the start, referred from an attorney or court, billing of insurance is not appropriate. Thus, in forensic settings, it may be the older adult, the attorney, or the court who pay for the forensic evaluation. It is up to the clinician to determine who is responsible for payment and what the specific procedure will be (i.e., payment of a retainer, etc.). Given the large amount of pre-assessment work that often needs to be done on these cases, it can be helpful for the psychologist to ask for an upfront fee for several hours to review records prior to giving an opinion on the necessity and pros or cons of a capacity evaluation.

V. General Approaches to Assessing the Older Adult

General Principles

Capacity assessments with older adults differ from regular clinical assessments in that they focus on a specific capacity question. Therefore, they require a functional assessment directed to relevant legal standards. In keeping with good clinical practice, tools employed in these assessments should be normed for older populations. Reference texts, such as the *Handbook of Normative Data for Neuropsychological Assessment* (Mitrushina, Boone, Razani, & D'Elia, 2005) and a *Compendium of Neuropsychological Tests* (Strauss, Sherman, & Spreen, 2006) provide up-to-date normative information on many general cognitive tests for older adults.

Is there a "core assessment battery" for capacity assessments? As the range of potential capacity questions varies so widely, as do the constituent functional and cognitive abilities, it is not possible to have a "core assessment battery." Instead, a flexible battery based on sound psychometric measures is required. Whenever possible psychologists should use functional tools that have been demonstrated to be psychometrically sound and normed for older adults.

> See **Appendix B** for a list and description of functional measures.

However, because capacity is an emerging practice area, there are a limited number of such tools available. Thus, psychologists will need to seek other sources of data in some instances, such as functional observations, collateral interviews, and multidisciplinary team input regarding function. The report for capacity assessments should be drafted specifically for this purpose and offer a clearly stated opinion regarding capacity. Sample reports in Chapter 6 provide examples of how to convey an opinion.

Clinical Interview

Although psychologists bring important abilities in the application of objective testing, the clinical interview remains an essential part of any capacity evaluation. However, the clinical interview may take on a different role in capacity assessments than it might in other assessments. It can be useful to follow the clinical framework introduced in Chapter 3 as part of the capacity interview. For example, in addition to performing a thorough psychiatric diagnostic interview, the capacity interview is an opportunity to gain information on the medical and cognitive presentation, everyday functioning, individual values and preferences, risk of harm, and means to enhance capacity that impact most cases. The following sections provide examples for how to modify the clinical interview for capacity assessments.

Assessing Functional Elements During the Clinical Interview

It is important to obtain functional information through interviews with the patient, and if appropriate, family and staff. Discrepancies between older adult reports of their IADLS and ADLs and collateral or objective reports can be especially revealing. (Of course, the psychologist would need to consider whether a collateral has a conflict of interest in describing functioning better or worse than it actually is—especially in a criminal case). For example, if being asked to assess financial capacity, asking the older adult to list sources of income, bank branches, and investments/retirement accounts to help ascertain their abilities. It may be that the older adult is able to handle simple financial transactions, but needs assistance with complex financial transactions.

Assessing the Diagnoses Producing Functional or Decisional Disability

The clinical interview should include questions to help determine if there is a medical, psychiatric, or neurological condition impacting cognition. An interview might include a history of the presenting problem, course, medical history, psychiatric history, substance/alcohol abuse, review of medications, and a review of symptoms.

See **Appendix F** for a list of medical conditions that can impact capacity.

Assessing Cognition During the Clinical Interview

Although cognitive testing will provide the standardized data to determine the presence or absence of impaired cognition, interview data can also provide a wealth of information regarding the nature and extent of the impairment. Many clinicians will begin with a brief mental status screening using an interview format or specific screening test to obtain a ballpark estimate of level of functioning. The screening test itself is limited in its ability to predict capacity because of its lack of sensitivity to executive functioning, but can be useful as a starting point and to help in the selection of assessment tools.

Behavioral evidence of memory and executive dysfunction may be apparent during the clinical interview and should be noted. In terms of memory impairment, one can include a discussion of current events or past important events (e.g., sports, politics, major disasters). It is also helpful to assess accuracy of autobiographical information, including noting if a temporal gradient is present (i.e., older adult is able to accurately report some historical information but not information from past year or so). Based on interview data it is often possible to determine if there is the presence of errors in recent versus remote memory. In terms of executive functioning, difficulties with initiation, flexibility, impulsivity, and lability throughout the discussion are noteworthy. Insight into the current situation, and any deficits is critical in being able to accept assistance and delegate to others.

Values and Preferences

A person's decisions should be understood in the context of lifestyle or life patterns, values, and preferences. Choices that are linked with lifetime values might be considered "rational" for an individual, even if outside the norm. For example, some individuals choose not to involve banks in any of their financial transactions, live in marginal housing, or use their income to support non-mainstream ideals. A person's values may arise from age, sexual orientation, race, ethnicity, gender, culture, religion, or other life experience that informs life perspective. For example, previous experiences in assisting others in end-of-life treatment decisions may affect the approach taken to one's own decisions.

Knowledge of values is not only important in informing capacity judgments, but also in the guardianship plan. Core values may impact the individual's preference for who is named guardian, as well as preferences concerning medical decisions, financial decisions, and living arrangements. What is needed are questions that allow a deep understanding of the reasons behind a person's choices. For example:

1. Think about what is most important to you in your life. What makes life meaningful or good for you now?
2. Consider what is important to you in relation to your health. What, if any, religious or personal beliefs do you have about sickness, health care decision-making, or dying?
3. What is your financial history? Are you in any debt? Do you live week to week? Are you able to plan ahead and save for the future? How do you prefer to spend money?
4. Where are you living now? How long have you been there? What makes a home a home for you?
5. Who are the family and/or friends that live in your community that are important to you? What about those that live in another community?

Other specific examples of questions to add to clinical interviews appear in Chapter 6.

Objective Testing: Functional

Capacity assessments involve the integration of data from cognitive and functional sources. In the past, older adult and/or collateral reports were primarily employed to examine the functional piece of the assessment. However, those reports may be biased by lack of insight or motivational issues. Newer approaches to functional capacities include direct observation of older adult's abilities, the use of functional measures abilities and functioning abilities, and structured interviews. Direct assessment of functional abilities can be performed by a psychologist as well as many allied health professionals. Occupational therapists have special training in assessing everyday functioning.

Capacity Assessment Tools

More recently, a number of clinicians and researchers have developed assessment tools that attempt to operationalize the legal standards for specific capacities into direct functional assessment instruments. The items and summary scales are not meant to replace a full clinical assessment, but may help the evaluator assess specific functional areas relevant to the capacity in question.

Medical Consent Capacity. Capacity to consent to medical treatment has seen the most instrument development, such as the MacArthur Competence Assessment Tool - Treatment (Grisso et al., 1998) and the Competency to Consent to Treatment Instrument (Marson et al., 1995). These are described in the medical consent capacity section of Chapter 6 and in Appendix B.

Sexual Consent Capacity. There are currently no standardized tools to assess sexual consent capacity.

Financial Capacity. Several tools exist for the psychologist to assess financial capacity, including the money management section of the Independent Living Scales (Loeb, 1996), which has norms for older adults, the Financial Capacity Instrument (Griffith et al., 2003; Marson et al., 2000), and the Hopemont Capacity Assessment Interview (Staats & Edelstein, 1995). These are described in the financial capacity section of Chapter 6 and in Appendix B.

Testamentary Capacity. There are currently no standardized tools to assess testamentary capacity.

Driving. The best "tool" for assessing driving is targeted in-office testing followed by simulator and on-road testing by a driving professional. As described in Chapter 6, there are some in-office tools that are important as part of a comprehensive driving assessment.

Independent Living. In addition to IADL/ADL tools, some instruments have been developed to assess independent living in the context of capacity questions, such as the Independent Living Scales (Loeb, 1996) and the Decision-making Interview for Guardianship (Anderer, 1997). These are described in the independent living capacity section of Chapter 6 and in Appendix B.

ADL/IADL Rating Scales

There are a wide variety of scales (see Appendix B) developed to assess an older adult's level of functioning for "Activities of Daily Living" (ADL) and "Instrumental Activities of Daily Living" (IADL). These can be useful in organizing and rating assessments of functioning within specific functional domains.

Objective Testing: Cognitive

Psychologists may employ a variety of tasks in the assessment of cognition. The "best" test battery will depend on the context, the setting, and the particulars of the case. The following information is provided as a review to psychologists with some task examples.

> Cognitive tests are listed
> in **Appendix C.**

Attention

The older adult's ability to attend to tasks is an important first step in the completion of an assessment. An inability to do so may be indicative of a delirious state. Tasks such as digit span or coding can help to determine a baseline for attentional abilities.

Language

An ability to express a choice is a critical component of capacity assessments. Complex medical and financial decisions require the ability to read and comprehend written documents. Speech production, language comprehension, and written language skills are all components of language assessment. Impairments in object naming may be indicative of a dementia process. Impairment in language production or comprehension may be indicative of an aphasia that may be secondary to a vascular injury.

A language sample can be obtained by asking an older adult to describe a scene. Language comprehension can be assessed by asking an older adult to follow commands. Object naming may be assessed by presenting an older adult with a line drawing and asking for the name of the object. A writing sample can indicate written language skills. The older adult could also be asked to read a sample and answer questions regarding the passage. If there is any indication of a frank language disturbance (i.e., Broca's aphasia), a more extensive formal assessment of language using a language-specific battery may be warranted.

Memory

Memory disorders can impair decision-making by influencing the older adult's ability to recall previously learned information, integrate information across choice options, and learn new information. Memory impairments are the hallmark of dementia processes and as such serve as a marker of potential impairment and further decline. Free recall, cued recall, and recognition are formats for memory assessment in verbal and visual memory domains. Referrals that include a history of traumatic brain injury may need to add additional assessments of post-traumatic amnesia (PTA).

List learning tasks are especially sensitive to mild cognitive impairment. A list learning task will provide information regarding immediate memory in the initial trials. After a delay, the task will provide information regarding free recall and possibly recognition abilities. These tasks may also allow for observation of specific memory errors, such as a tendency to perseverate and/or confabulate. Story recall memory tasks are useful because they provide information regarding how older adults remember information within a context. Visual memory tasks can provide a perceptual construction (drawing) sample, as well as an assessment of visual memory abilities. Taken together, the clinician can provide a profile of strengths and weaknesses and make recommendations for maximizing capacity. For

example, the psychologist may report that "the older adult was impaired on tasks of verbal free recall, but performed much better with a recognition format. The older adult will perform best if information is provided to her in a written format." Or, the psychologist may report

the older adult performed poorly on a list learning task that included many intrusions. On a story memory task, the older adult tended to confabulate, including many extraneous details. Thus, the older adult is a poor historian, has difficulty learning new information, and has a tendency to "fill in the gaps," which potentially impacts decisional capacity.

Visual-Perceptual

Perceptual disturbances can impair a person's capacity to drive and potentially impair abilities to complete financial calculations. A clinical assessment in such cases might include tools that assess an older adult's ability to copy figures, decipher or match patterns, and/or construct objects to samples.

Speed of Processing

Slowed speed of processing can result in vulnerabilities to poor decision making, especially in the context of coercive interactions. A clinical assessment may include tools that assess processing speed, such as Digit-Symbol Coding from the WAIS, coding from the RBANS, or Trails A from the trail-making test.

Executive Functioning

Executive functioning components, such as the ability to plan, think flexibly, respond to feedback, and inhibit impulsive responses are critical to effective decision making. Some common tools used in clinical geropsychology settings, such as the MMSE, RBANS, and COGNISTAT, EXIT25, provide limited information regarding executive functioning. Thus, supplemental tests of executive function should be employed whenever there is a question regarding decision-making capacity.

Judgment and Reasoning

Tasks assessing judgment and reasoning can be important auxiliary measures when developing your opinion regarding an older adult's capacity. Tasks that assess abstract reasoning like the Similarities subtest of the WAIS tests can provide a helpful assessment of thought processes. Judgment tasks like the Kaplan Practical Problem Solving Task, or reasoning from the COGNISTAT can provide a sample of problem solving abilities. It can be especially helpful to look at the distinction between responses to these posed problems and abilities to implement them. For example, when posed the hypothetical problem "What would you do if you saw smoke and fire in the home," the older adult may answer "run and put it out" ignoring mobility issues.

Objective Testing: Psychopathology

A variety of objective measures of psychopathology can be used to supplement information obtained via the interview and mental status examination. The objective assessment of older adults can be challenging, as individuals of this cohort are less familiar with formal testing, many of the measures used to assess psychopathology among younger adults lack psychometric support with older adults, and the presentations and prevalence of psychopathology can be different in older than younger adults (e.g., Cohen et al., 2000; Depp & Jeste, 2004; Fisk & O'Riley, 2008; Kogan, Edelstein, & McKee, 2000). One should limit the use of objective measures to those that have been created explicitly for older adults and have psychometric support, and those that were developed for younger adults and have accumulated satisfactory psychometric support with older adults. Two resources are Edelstein et al. (2008), a review of instruments for the assessment of selected disorders and problems (i.e., anxiety, depression, personality, sleep, suicide), and Segal, Coolidge, O'Riley & Heinz (2006), a review of structured and semi-structured interview instruments.

Lengthy, comprehensive assessment instruments (e.g., MMPI) can be helpful, but often exact the costs of fatigue and diminished attention with older adults. This can be particularly problematic with individuals whom one already suspects may have compromised cognitive skills. The use of more targeted assessment instruments based on available information and the initial interview results is likely to prove more efficient and less taxing.

It is important to avoid placing too much emphasis on psychiatric diagnostic categories when attempting to appreciate the effects of psychiatric and emotional factors on capacity. Rather, the focus should ultimately be on the potential influence of the psychiatric and emotional symptoms on capacity. This influence can occur through the patient's cognitive processes (e.g., delusional thinking, judgment, insight), through diminished cognitive skills (e.g., impaired attention, impaired working memory), or through behaviors (e.g., disinhibition).

For example, an older adult with schizophrenia might hold a delusion that his or her physician is attempting to poison him with the medication being offered. This delusion may not influence the ability to express a choice, the ability to understand information relevant to his or her treatment, or the ability to reason with relevant information. However, the delusion could affect the ability to appreciate the significance of the information provided about the medication for his or her disorder and treatment if he believed that the medication would not improve his or her condition. Moreover, it could influence the person's ability to appreciate the probable consequences of the treatment option that is being offered. That is, the patient believes that the medicine being offered is poison that will kill.

As another example, an older adult with active Bipolar I disorder may have manic episodes with racing thoughts, rapid speech, decreased need for sleep, hypersexuality, euphoria, and grandiosity. These symptoms might influence capacity in any number of ways. Sleep deprivation associated with the disorder could affect sustained attention and working memory, and impact the ability to understand information, appreciate the significance of information, and reason with the relevant information during a manic episode. Also, the behaviors themselves, such as excessive spending, could directly influence capacity—such as the ability to manage a business.

The Role of Collateral Interviews

Clinicians accustomed to working with older adults already know the value of conducting collateral interviews in order to ascertain the older adult's insight and areas of concern. In the capacity interview, these interviews take on added importance as a source of potentially objective data regarding the older adult's functional abilities. Multidisciplinary team members may serve as collaterals. It is necessary to obtain the older adult's permission to interview collaterals.

However, with any particular case, there may be family members with strongly differing opinions and motives regarding the outcome of the assessment. For example, in cases involving potential guardianship, there may be some family members who oppose such an action and others advocating for the protection. It is the clinician's role to ascertain the motives of the family members involved in the case and the implications for the collateral data. For example, sometimes family members become concerned regarding the financial management of a parent if one child (often the caregiver) appears to be benefiting financially from the arrangement. Conversely, it is sometimes the in-home caregiver who has the most information regarding a decline that drives the proceedings despite a lack of concern from out-of-state adult children. In criminal matters, adult dependent children or paid caregivers may be alleged suspects in financial abuse cases, and thus have motives to misrepresent the presentation.

Post Evaluation

How Will My Capacity Report Be Used?

A capacity report is subject to multiple uses. It may be informational and advisory, it may direct clinical action, or it could be used as evidence in a court hearing or trial. During the pre-assessment phase, the psychologist will hopefully have determined who would be serving as the client and where the report will be submitted. However, it is possible for cases to

evolve and for the report to be subject to additional uses. The report that was originally meant to be used as informational may ultimately end up as evidence in a judicial setting. The capacity evaluation may also inform a plan of care for the older adult, and could specifically be used in a "guardianship plan" developed by a guardian for the older adult.

Do I Use a Special Form?

In some states, an additional legally mandated form needs to be completed if the report is for guardianship. These forms should be completed in addition to a complete clinical evaluation and can be submitted together.

Will I Provide Oral Testimony?

In most instances, a written report will be sufficient. Occasionally, in a case of contested capacity or in criminal matters, a psychologist might be asked to provide oral testimony in the court. Suggestions for preparation as an expert witness are provided in Chapter 8.

How Do I Integrate the Information?

At the completion of the assessment, the psychologist must now form an opinion regarding an individual's capacity. In doing so, the psychologist will consider a wide range of evidence, including functional skills relevant to the capacity in question, cognitive functioning, psychiatric functioning, medical diagnoses and prognosis, the individual's values, and situational risks relevant to the capacity. This requires a careful weighing of these factors in order to arrive, if possible, at a clear yes/no opinion regarding capacity. However, there will occasionally be borderline cases in which clinically the best judgment may be a finding of "marginal capacity." Marginal capacity findings have value as long as they are based on evidence and not on the clinician's reluctance to offer a clear opinion on the matter. A court (if involved) will be able to consider a clinical finding of marginal capacity in its overall calculus in arriving at a legal capacity judgment.

In weighing the different sources of evidence, it is best for the clinician to focus initially on evidence regarding the functional abilities constituent to the capacity, as this is the evidence that is most capacity specific. Secondary levels of evidence include cognitive and psychiatric functioning, and medical diagnosis and prognosis, which are each relevant to capacity but not by themselves dispositive of capacity issues. However, they obviously are relevant to the clinical capacity judgment, particularly in non-retrospective evaluations where the underlying diagnostic issues may alter the functional abilities and associated risks in the future. As part of formulating a capacity judgment, consideration should be given to the individual's values and their relation to his/her behavior, and also to the specific risks inherent to the capacity situation. It is also important to describe available means of enhancing an individual's capacity, if such means are available and feasible.

As an example, in the case of evaluating treatment consent capacity, a clinician should first evaluate the functional abilities constituent to this capacity. These would be the patient's abilities to express a treatment choice, to understand the treatment situation and options, to reason about treatment choices and respective risks/benefits, and to appreciate the personal consequence of a treatment decision. The clinician should then consider this functional evidence in relation to the patient's medical conditions, prognoses, cognitive functioning (e.g., neuropsychological test performance), and psychiatric functioning (e.g., clinical interview and psychiatric or personality testing information). In formulating the judgment, all this evidence should be considered in light of the patient's value system, and also in relation to the relative risks/benefits of the treatment and social situation. The clinician's overall analysis and judgment should be shaped by the individual's strong values (e.g., desire to avoid being a burden to others) risk/benefit ratio of the medical situation and proposed treatment (e.g., a high risk surgery versus a low-risk biopsy).

The clinical findings and capacity judgment made should be framed within the general context of any applicable legal standards, in order to ensure that the clinical findings are closely linked to the decisional framework and processes of the court. At the same time, in stating clinical findings and judgments, the clinician should be careful to not invade the province of the court, and to clearly identify his/her decision and findings as clinical and not legal capacity matters.

How Do I Present Information in a Report?

Each psychologist will use his or her own format for report writing. Examples of reports—and different formats—appear in Chapter 6. A conclusion section of a capacity report will likely address multiple issues.

Diagnostic Impressions. A psychologist may begin a report conclusion by addressing the diagnosis—much like in a typical clinical referral. For example, it might include cognitive/neuropsychologcal findings and personality findings and conclude with a DSM "five axis" format.

Capacity Opinion. The next section or sections can present the clinician's opinion of the older adult's psycholegal capacities. This section should specifically address the capacity at issue and, when possible, provide a clear yes/no judgment regarding the opinion.

Recommendations. Finally, a clinician can detail specific recommendations that may help to optimize decision making and/or improve clinical care.

Case Examples of Conclusions

The following case examples are to demonstrate how one arrives at a specific statement of capacity. These examples are intended to illustrate key points in arriving at a clinical judgment. *These examples do not represent a full report*, which likely include detailed information regarding the person's history, clinical interview, standardized testing, medical record, etc. More detailed examples are provided in the specific capacity sections of Chapter 6.

Case Example 1

The first example draws from a case where the psychologist is being asked to give an opinion regarding the older adult's ability to manage her finances in a retrospective determination. The older adult has a history of adequate knowledge and skills regarding her financial transactions, but these have declined significantly in recent years. The psychologist is being asked about her ability to make a large financial transaction in the recent past.

It is this psychologist's opinion that Ms. Smith did not have the capacity to manage her simple and complex finances independently, and was not able to perform these financial tasks in July 2007 until the present. Her current diagnosis (dementia of the Alzheimer's type, moderate stage) and cognitive functioning (severely impaired memory) suggests that her memory loss has been present for at least 2-3 years. Further, Ms. Smith scored in the low range on a task designed to assess her financial ability. It is this examiner's opinion that Ms. Smith is not able to make small purchases, write checks, or read or understand her bank statements without assistance at present. Further, she is not able to manage her complex finances, balance her checkbook, or sign real-estate agreements.

Case Example 2

The next example presents a case of an older adult's ability to continue to manage his finances in the face of clear cognitive decline. He has a strong history of knowledge and skills in this arena and as yet, no evidence of errors in financial management. He has explicitly delegated these responsibilities and can continue to manage with support.

It is this psychologist's opinion that Mr. Jones is able to manage his simple and complex finances independently. His current diagnosis, mild traumatic brain injury, has resulted in moderately impaired memory and executive functioning. However, he performed in the high range on a functional assessment of financial abilities. Mr. Jones has fairly well-preserved abilities in terms of financial management secondary to his background in accounting. Further, Mr. Jones has on-line banking set up to manage most of his monthly bills and direct deposit of his assets. For more complex transactions, such as managing his investment portfolio, Mr. Jones may benefit from assistance. The current protections in place,

with his son as POA and an investment advisor to assist with his retirement income, appear appropriate.

Case Example 3

In this example, the older adult also presents with clear moderate cognitive impairment. However, the client does not have the strong history of skills in this arena and there is evidence of recent financial abuse. The example illustrates how a psychologist may arrive at a different clinical opinion when considering objective data in light of the context and case particulars.

It is this psychologist's opinion that Mr. Roberts does not have capacity to manage simple and complex finances independently. His current diagnosis, vascular dementia, has resulted in moderately impaired memory and executive functioning. Mr. Roberts performed in the moderate range on a functional assessment of financial abilities, able to complete simple calculations, but unable to do multiple step transactions. Mr. Roberts has already been a victim of fraud. He appeared to remember that he had signed some type of document, but did not appreciate its permanent nature and the risks to his estate. Mr. Roberts is highly susceptible to fraud and exploitation in his current state and would benefit from a conservator to protect his assets.

Case Example 4

The case illustrates how a psychologist may arrive at a decision when an older adult presents with minimal impairment and has adequate skills to manage transactions. The example illustrates the consideration of test data in view of the person's history and values.

It is this psychologist's opinion that Ms. Wright does have the capacity to manage her simple and complex finances independently. Ms. Wright's daughter reported that Ms. Wright had recently given $50,000 to a charity and questioned her financial decision-making abilities. Ms. Wright has a history of diabetes and hypertension placing her at increased risk for vascular dementia. She performed in the low average range on tests of memory and executive functioning. However, she performed in the high range on a functional assessment of financial abilities. She reported that she had given to this charity for over 20 years. She was able to describe the impact that this gift would have on her standard of living (minimal). Thus, Ms. Wright does not need formal protections in place at the current time.

Case Example 5

The final case example provides a possible format for the presentation of evaluation data, including diagnostic impressions, capacity conclusions, and recommendations.

Diagnostic Impressions

The results of the clinical interview, neuropsychological testing, and review of medical records reveal neurocognitive patterns consistent with a traumatic brain injury to the frontal lobes of moderate to severe severity.

Cognitively, *he has adequate attention. Visual perceptual abilities were not assessed due to bilateral visual impairment related to his brain injury. His language production, comprehension, and naming were within normal limits.*

Mr. Brown had deficits in memory, executive functioning, and reasoning. Mr. Brown has no memory of the event itself. This occurs because the part of the brain involved in encoding (the hippocampus region in the medial temporal lobes) cannot encode the event secondary to trauma. Second, Mr. Brown has minimal retrograde amnesia, or a loss of memory for past events. Third, Mr. Brown has post-traumatic amnesia lasting for several months following the brain injury. Finally, Mr. Brown has significant anterograde amnesia, or an inability to learn new information. His performance improves when given repetitions and cues, but he tends to confabulate or fill in the gaps unintentionally.

In terms of executive functioning and reasoning, because of Mr. Brown s brain injury to the frontal lobes, he has poor insight into his limitations. He had difficulty solving everyday problems and abstract problems. He had difficulty with initiation. He will have trouble thinking flexibly about a problem and may get stuck on a particular solution. He may be impulsive in his judgments.

Emotionally, *Mr. Brown has reported numerous symptoms of depression during the clinical interview, and his mood was depressed. He scored a 9 / 15 on the Geriatric Depression Scale-short form indicating moderate depression.*

DSM-IV-TR Diagnosis:

Axis I	*Dementia due to Head trauma; Mood disorder due to a general medical condition.*
Axis II	*No diagnosis*
Axis III	*Bilateral Visual Impairment*
Axis IV	*Fraud victim legal action pending*
Axis V	*GAF = 40*

Capacity Conclusions

The results of functional testing previously described, combined with reports of staff, family, occupational therapy assessment, and considered in light of the neuropsychological testing support the following findings.

Financial Capacity: *Given Mr. Brown s moderate to severe impairments in memory, executive function, and on direct assessment of financial capacities (money management scale of the Independent Living Scales), it is the examiner s opinion that Mr. Brown does not have capacity to manage simple or complex finances independently.*

Capacity to Manage His Person: *Given Mr. Brown s moderate to severe impairments in memory and executive function, and on direct assessment of reasoning in independent living tasks, it is this examiner s opinion that Mr. Brown is currently at significant risk for harm to himself. He has limited insight into his abilities and his injuries. Mr. Brown needs the structure of 24-hour care at the present time and for the foreseeable future.*

Recommendations

Mr. Brown has impairments in memory and executive functioning that impact his simple and complex decision making. He will continue to need assistance for both personal and financial decisions.

1. *At this interview, depression was evident. His treatment regimen for depression should be reviewed and potentially adjusted.*
2. *Mr. Brown is now 12 months post injury. Much of his recovery has already occurred, so at this point a shift from treatment to compensatory training should be considered.*
3. *Mr. Brown can still express preferences and these should be honored when appropriate. When stable, Mr. Brown would enjoy visitors. He would enjoy visits with his dog, if that is acceptable to the facility. Many facilities have pet therapy available.*

Capacity Worksheet for Psychologists

Source: Assessment of Older Adults with Diminished Capacity: A Handbook for Psychologists by the ABA Commission on Law and Aging and the American Psychological Association (2008). Please read and review the handbook prior to using the worksheet.

Name: _____   Date(s) of Evaluation: _____

Psychologist: _____   Place of Evaluation: _____

A. Pre-Assessment Screening

Issue	Questions to consider
What functional and decisional capacities are in question:	What types of decisional or functional processes are in question? What data are needed? Am I appropriately qualified to assess these?
Who is involved in this case:	Who is the client? Who are the interested parties? Who is requesting the evaluation? Who sees the report? Is the court or litigants involved?
Who is the older adult:	What is the person's history, age, cultural background, primary language, sensory functioning?
When does this evaluation need to be completed:	How urgent is the request? Is there a court date? What is the time frame of interest?
Where and how will the evaluation take place:	In what setting does the evaluation take place? What accommodations are needed to maximize performance?
Why is this question being raised:	Why now? What is the history of the case? Will a capacity evaluation resolve the problem? Have all less restrictive alternatives and interventions been exhausted?
Is the patient medically stable:	Have all temporary and reversible causes of cognitive confusion been assessed and treated?

B. Informed Consent

Understanding:	Issues to disclose
	Why is the evaluation requested? Procedures involved in evaluation? Potential risks? Potential benefits? Uses of the report? Limits on privacy and confidentiality?

☐ Understands and consents   ☐ Questionable understanding but assents
☐ Understands and refuses   ☐ Questionable understanding but refuses

C. Setting up the Assessment: Legal Standard and Functional Elements

What is the legal standard for the capacity in question?
What are the functional elements to consider?

D. Record Review

Medical records	Diagnoses Laboratory Tests Imaging Other Treatments Medications
Legal records	Documents filed in the court Financial statements HCP/POAHC documents
Other Records	

E. Collateral Interviews

Family
Staff/ Professional Caregivers
Other

F. Accommodating and Enhancing Capacity During the Assessment

Assess recent events and losses, such as bereavement
Explore medical factors such as nutrition, medications, hydration
Select tests inconsideration of cultural and language issues; Administer tests in primary language
Select tests that are validated for the age of the person
Assess ability to read and accommodate reading difficulties
Adjust seating, lighting; Use visual and hearing aids
Consider fatigue; Take breaks; Use multiple testing sessions

G. Assessment Data

Functional elements (list from 4B above):	☐ Objective Assessment	☐ Clinical Interview

1. _____
Level of impairment:
Describe:
2. _____
Level of impairment:
Describe:
3. _____
Level of impairment:
Describe:
4. _____
Level of impairment:
Describe:

Cognitive Underpinnings (possible domains): ☐ Objective Assessment	☐ Clinical Interview

1. Sensory Acuity

2. Motor Activity and Speed of processing

3. Attention and Concentration

4. Working memory

5. Short term/recent memory and Learning

6. Long term memory

7. Understanding or Receptive Language

8. Communication or Expressive Language

9. Arithmetic

10. Verbal Reasoning

11. Visual-Spatial and Visuo-Constructional Reasoning

12. Executive Functioning

13. Other

Psychiatric/Emotional Factors (possible domains):	☐ Objective Assessment	☐ Clinical Interview

1. Disorganized Thinking

2. Hallucinations

3. Delusions

4. Anxiety

5. Mania

6. Depressed Mood

7. Insight

8. Impulsivity

9. Noncompliance

10. Other

Values	Possible Considerations
	What is the older adult's view of the situation?
	Preferences for how decisions made? And by whom?
	Preferences for living setting?
	Goals including self assessment of quality of life?
	Concerns, fears, preferences, religious views?
	Preferences for spending and saving?
	Impact of culture, age, sexual orientation, diversity?
	Views about guardianship (if applicable)?
Risks	**Possible Considerations**
	Is the risk new or old?
	How serious is the risk?
	How imminent is the risk?
	What is the risk of harm to self? To others?
	Are there concrete instances of failure?
	How objective is the assessment of risk?

H. Findings

Diagnoses and Prognoses	Possible Considerations
	What diagnoses account for the deficits?
	Can conditions be treated?
	Are deficits likely to get better, worse or stay the same?
	When should the older adult be re-evaluated?

Capacity Framework	Capacity Conclusions
1) The functional abilities constituent to the capacity; 2) Cognitive abilities, psychiatric/emotional functioning, and medical diagnoses and prognosis, *as they relate to the functional abilities*; 3) The individual's values, social network, and the specific risks of the capacity situation.	☐ Has capacity for decision / task in question ☐ Lacks capacity for decision / task in question ☐ Has marginal capacity for decision / task in question (if the case is not being adjudicated, recommended course of action)

Steps to Enhance Capacity	Would the Older Adult benefit from:
	Education, training, or rehabilitation?
	Mental health treatment?
	Occupational, physical, or other therapy?
	Home and/or social services?
	Assistive devices or accommodations?
	Medical treatment, operation or procedure?
	Other?

VI. Assessing Specific Capacities

This chapter presents six specific capacities: medical consent, sexual consent, financial capacity, testamentary capacity, driving, and independent living. In each section we will present the legal standards and discuss functional, cognitive, psychiatric, and diagnostic factors, as well as the role of values, risk, and enhancing capacity. Each section includes a case example. For each section one author took the lead; therefore the case examples reflect the approach of one clinician, although the working group and our expert panel provided input. Therefore, this chapter provides some diversity of approaches to formatting a clinical approach and related report.

Medical Consent

Introduction

The doctrine of informed consent requires clinicians to obtain voluntary and competent agreement to a medical intervention prior to performing the intervention, and only after the patient has been informed of the material risks, benefits, and other facts of the condition and procedure.

In the area of health care a variety of capacities might be raised—such as the capacity to consent to a specific medical treatment, the capacity to manage one's healthcare and medications, and the capacity to appoint a healthcare proxy (a decision maker for one's healthcare in the event of incapacity). This chapter focuses on capacity to consent to treatment, after brief comments on related medical capacity issues below.

Capacity to Manage Health

The capacity to manage one's health and medications is an important area related to the capacity to live independently (discussed later in this chapter) and is little studied.

Capacity to Appoint a Health Care Proxy

As noted in Chapter 2, the capacity to execute an advance directive for health care is quite different than the capacity to make specific medical decisions, thought to be parallel to the capacity to contract. That is, it does not involve understanding and consenting to medical treatment but identifying a person to speak on one's behalf. This capacity sometimes arises in conjunction with the capacity to consent to treatment—particularly when a person is felt to be too impaired to consent to a treatment or procedure, and does not have a healthcare proxy appointed. In these situations the question sometimes arises whether the person still could have the capacity to appoint a decision maker. There is limited legal, conceptual, or empirical data on this topic (Allen et al., 2003). As noted, it is conceptually distinct from the capacity to consent to treatment, which is the focus of this section.

Extraordinary Medical Treatment

Many state laws and local hospital policies limit the authority of guardians and healthcare proxies to consent to extraordinary treatment, such as decisions to withdraw life-sustaining therapies (ventilation, artificial feeding and hydration), commit for mental health treatment, and consent to abortion, sterilization, administration of psychotropic medications, amputation, and electroconvulsive therapy. Typically these treatments require review by court or another oversight body (e.g., ethics committee). If a clinician is being asked to evaluate someone's capacity to consent to or refuse these treatments, and the question is being raised about possible proxy consent, clinicians should be familiar with any statutory requirements and local hospital policies regarding these situations.

This chapter will focus on the capacity to consent to ordinary medical treatment.

Legal Standard

Incapacity As Defined in Surrogate Health Care Decision-Making Statutes

A variety of statutory frameworks exist for defining incapacity in healthcare decision making, including the health care power of attorney and "living will," surrogate consent, and guardianship statutes. In these statutes, surrogate health care decision-making authority is triggered by a patient's lack of capacity to give informed consent for treatment.

For example, the Uniform Health-Care Decisions Act (a model law defining incapacity in the context of when a health care surrogate decision maker may be appointed) defines capacity as "the ability to understand significant benefits, risks, and alternatives to proposed health care and to make and communicate a health-care decision" (Uniform Health-Care Decisions Act, 1994). State-by-state citations for living will and health care power of attorney statutes can be viewed on the Web site of the ABA Commission on Law and Aging at http://www.abanet.org/aging.

Case Law Standards for Capacity to Consent

In addition to statutes, incapacity is defined in standards found in case law, used either individually or conjointly as a so-called "compound standard" (Berg, Appelbaum, Lidz, & Parker, 2001; Grisso et al., 1998), as detailed in the "functional" section below.

Substitute Judgment Mechanisms and Less Restrictive Alternatives

When individuals are believed to lack the capacity to make medical decisions, several options are available. A previously appointed health care proxy or durable power of attorney may make decisions, and in over 35 states next of kin may provide consent under defined circumstances even if not previously so appointed. In some cases, local policies allow for surrogate consent by hospital medical directors or ethics' committees.

Functional Elements

The ability to consent to medical treatment involves "functional" abilities that are cognitive in nature. Generally, in describing the functional elements of consent capacity, four case law standards commonly recognized to convey capacity are used, as described below.

1. Expressing a Choice

The standard of expressing a choice refers to patients who are seen to lack capacity because they cannot communicate a treatment choice, or vacillate to such an extent in their choice that it is seen to reflect a decisional impairment.

2. Understanding

The standard of understanding refers to the ability to comprehend diagnostic and treatment-related information and has been recognized in many states as fundamental to capacity.

3. Appreciation

The standard of appreciation has been interpreted in different ways. It has been described as the ability to relate treatment information to one's personal situation. The standard of appreciation especially reflects the ability to infer the possible benefits of treatment, as well as accept or believe the diagnosis. This standard has been related to the concepts of insight and foresight.

4. Reasoning

The standard of reasoning involves the ability to state rational explanations or to process information in a logically or rationally consistent manner.

Diagnostic Considerations

The capacity to consent to treatment has been most widely studied in dementia, and to a lesser extent in adults with psychotic disorders (although these studies do not focus on older adults). In mean comparisons with healthy controls, consent capacity of individuals with dementia is reduced compared to healthy controls (Kim, et al., 2002; Marson et al., 1995; Moye, Karel, Azar, & Gurrera, 2004a). Specific abilities affected by dementia are the capacity to understand information and to weigh the risks and benefits. In these same studies, the capacity to personally appreciate the diagnosis and the risks and benefits of treatment was sometimes impaired in older adults with dementia.

In control-comparison studies with individuals with schizophrenia, results are mixed, with some studies showing impairment relative to controls and others not; however these studies focus on younger adults with schizophrenia (Grisso et al., 1995; Wong, Clare, Holland, Watson, & Gunn, 2000). In general, the pattern of decisional impairment associated with schizophrenia is quite variable.

Adults in long-term care, without regard to specific diagnosis, have been noted to have high rates (44% - 69%) of medical consent capacity impairment (Barton, Mallik, Orr, & Janofsky, 1996; Fitten et al. 1990; Pruchno, Smyer, Rose, Hartman-Stein, & Lairbee-Henderson, 1995; Royall, Cordes, & Polk, 1997). More research is needed about consent impairments in other diagnostic conditions.

Cognitive Underpinnings

The relationship of cognitive functions and specific consent abilities has been studied in older adults with dementia. Diminished consent capacity has been associated with impairments in memory, executive functions, and comprehension. Specifically, difficulties in understanding diagnostic and treatment information has been strongly related to impaired memory, as well as impaired conceptualization, and comprehension (Gurrera et al., 2006; Marson et al., 1996; Marson et al., 1995). Appreciation has been less robustly related to cognitive functions than other consent abilities, but, perhaps not surprisingly, has been linked to impaired executive functions and conceptualization. Reasoning, involving contrasting risks and benefits and relating them to personal preferences has been associated with executive abilities, such as attention, mental flexibility, and the ability to recall information after a delay. Expressing a choice is a basic consent ability, and has been related to auditory comprehension and confrontation naming.

Psychiatric and Emotional Factors

Although the research literature suggests that consent abilities do not form a strict hierarchy (e.g., understanding is needed for appreciation is needed for reasoning), the ability to reason through risks and benefits appears to be the most cognitively complex task, involving remembering risks and benefits of various options (or at least being able to refer to them on paper), and weighing them against individual values and preferences. For example, a person might need to consider how much a specific treatment might affect those areas important to him or her—avoiding pain, avoiding dependency, or being able to pursue a desired activity. Because of the cognitive demands of this task, especially for complex treatments, or situations where there are multiple treatment options, when symptoms of depression or anxiety become severe, these psychiatric symptoms may affect the ability to reason.

In contrast, while symptoms associated with psychotic disorders may certainly affect a person's ability to understand and reason about information, psychotic disorders may especially impact "appreciation"—particularly when the patient is delusional. That is, symptoms of paranoid disorders may make it difficult to accept a specific diagnosis or the possibility that treatment will be beneficial.

Values

The position of a set of values and goals is foundational to capacity (President's Commission for the Study of Ethical Problems in Medicine and Biomedical and Behavioral Research, 1982). The idea here is that in the process of choosing among treatment alternatives a person is motivated by factors that define quality of life for that person, or that are broadly important in life—such as religious values, a desire to preserve life, a strong need for autonomy and independence, and a concern about being a burden on others.

A related set of commentary on the issue of values can be found in the ABA's 2002 Model Rules of Professional Conduct (http://www.abanet.org/cpr/mrpc). These rules describe for lawyers the factors to be balanced in the determination of capacity—including "the consistency of a decision with the known long-term commitments and values of the adult" (ABA, 2002). In this comment the ABA suggests that the consistency of a decision with values may be one important indicator of a person's capacity. Of course, values and related decisions also change over time—so fluctuating statements of values do not necessarily indicate incapacity. However, patients with dementia may be able to express consistent values, even when they are not fully able to engage in all the technical aspects of consent (Karel et al., 2007).

A variety of specific "values" have been identified as important to healthcare decision making. Patients may consider whether various treatment outcomes comprise states "worse than death" or otherwise affect quality of life in unacceptable ways (Ditto, Druley, Moore, Danks, & Smucker, 1996; Lawton et al., 1999; Pearlman et al., 1993); such values ratings are predictive of treatment choices (Ditto et al., 1996; Fischer, Alpert, Stoeckle, & Emanuel, 1997; Patrick et al., 1997; Schonwetter, Walker, Solomon, Indurkhya, & Robinson, 1996). Similarly, treatment choices can be made in view of how they affect valued relationships. Patients are often very concerned about the impact of the illness and treatment on loved ones, with many older adults in particular expressing concern about becoming a burden to their families (Karel & Gatz, 1996). Individuals may differ in the extent to which they desire control over treatment decisions, based on generational, cultural, and personality factors. Older cohorts and some cultural groups believe decision making authority rests with the doctor or the family.

Risk Considerations

A "sliding scale" for capacity has been proposed when balancing risk considerations and the threshold for intervention. A relatively low level of capacity may be needed for a relatively low risk procedure. For example, a cognitively impaired patient in a nursing home may be more likely to be viewed as having the capacity to consent to a low-risk procedure, such as a standard blood draw, as compared to a high-risk procedure, such as an invasive surgery like coronary artery bypass graft. The evaluator will want to consider the risks associated with the procedure, and the risk associated with not doing the procedure, as well as the likelihood of these outcomes. In addition to these considerations, the evaluator may consider the risk associated with delaying a decision to consent to a medical procedure. For example, it may be possible to delay a hernia repair surgery if a person is refusing that surgery, and it is felt that some clinical intervention may enhance capacity (e.g., treating depression or anxiety; addressing causes of delirium).

When known, it is useful to consider risks in tandem with individual values. For example, if a person is refusing a potentially life saving procedure that could also lead to significant functional impairment, ascertaining what is known about the person's values regarding sustaining life versus quality of life is critical. Some risk considerations become especially challenging in the very old, particularly in considering the risks and negative outcomes associated with a procedure. For example, surgery to correct a slowly progressing spinal compression may carry more risks than the slow progression over time for a very aged individual. Therefore, the evaluator will need to carefully consider the level of capacity needed to consent to a treatment or procedure, in view of a careful weighing of the risks of intervention versus non-intervention and how these risks compare to the person's values.

Steps to Enhance Capacity

As with any psychological evaluation, and any capacity evaluation, the evaluator should strive to maximize the person's abilities during assessment by addressing sensory deficits and, when possible, evaluating the individual when most alert and awake. Of course, medical consent capacity evaluations may occur in acute medical situations where it is not possible to wait, for example, until the time of day when the individual is functioning best.

Decision-making capacity evaluations aiming to optimize decisional abilities should utilize disclosure formats that are simplified and guided to enhance understanding (Dunn & Jeste, 2001; Taub et al., 1987). These may closely mimic good doctor-patient dialogues in which information is presented in a manner that maximizes patient participation, as compared to a test-like situation where a patient is required to memorize information. Providing the information in writing, in short phrases, and, with diagrams may enhance understanding of the procedure. Capacity evaluations should not neglect to consider the affect of framing, order, and phrasing on the decision-making process. Framing refers to whether risks are described as the likelihood of negative outcome versus positive outcome (e.g., "there is a 10% chance you will die" versus "there is a 90% chance you will live"). Further, evaluators might consider the role of anxiety in decision-making. For example, is the individual feeling overwhelmed by the amount of medical information and anxious about possible outcomes that he or she is not processing information optimally?

Clinical Judgments of Consent Capacity

In a seminal study, Marson et al., (1997) found low agreement (kappa = .14) between five physicians with different specialty training who provided dichotomous ratings of consent capacity in older adults with Alzheimer's disease. Agreement improved when physicians were trained to evaluate specific legal standards (kappa = .48), but there was still considerable variability (Marson et al., 2000). It is unclear what leads to different clinical judgments between different clinicians, but some factors have been suggested.

A wide range of characteristics has been noted to influence clinical judgments in diagnostic processes, such as gender (Roter & Hall, 2004), patient-physician racial concordance (Cooper et al., 2003), verbal and nonverbal behaviors (Beck, Daughtridge, & Sloane, 2002; Roter, Frankel, Hall, & Sluyter, 2006), and respect for or liking of patients (Beach, Roter, Wang, Duggan, & Cooper, 2006; Hall, Horgan, Stein, & Roter, 2002). Although not yet studied in relation to capacity per se, related research shows that biases and emotional factors affect physician diagnostic judgment, and may lead to diagnostic errors (Graber,

Franklin, & Gordon, 2005; Groopman, 2007). With respect to particular medical decisions, clinicians may evaluate a patient's quality of life differently, and often as less desirable, than does the patient (Starr, Pearlmann, & Uhlmann, 1986; Uhlmann, Pearlman, & Cain, 1988; Uhlmann & Pearlmann, 1991), and physician proxies are poor at predicting patient's treatment preferences (Uhlmann et al., 1991). In evaluating capacity, clinicians may focus in on different cognitive abilities thought to be key (Earnst, Marson, & Harrell, 2000).

These findings point to the inherent nature of clinical judgment as representing an individualized decisional process, and one that may be influenced by bias factors, particularly in trying to understand the extent to which the risks associated with consent or refusal of procedure relates to the patient's values, cognitive functions, and decisional abilities.

In forming clinical judgments of consent capacity it may be useful to consider the diagnosis causing the consent impairment, the level of impairment within key cognitive abilities, such as memory, set shifting, naming, conceptualization, and the extent to which these translate to strengths or weaknesses in specific consent abilities of understanding, appreciation, reasoning, and expressing a choice. Many clinicians find that when a consent capacity evaluation is structured in this way, the process of forming a clinical judgment is more evident and defensible than a more unstructured clinical interview or mental status evaluation. In particular, it can be difficult to relate functioning on general mental status variables (e.g., orientation to day) to consent if the evaluator has not used some systematic approach to assessing consent abilities.

Clinical Approaches to Assessing Consent Capacity

Like any evaluation of civil capacities, the evaluation should focus especially on the relevant functional abilities.

Functional Assessment Instruments

In terms of assessing specific consent abilities, the area of consent capacity has seen the most extensive instrument development in comparison to other areas of civil capacity.

In addition to the nine instruments noted here, there are several other vignette assessment approaches described in the research literature (e.g., Allen et al., 2003; Fitten et al., 1990; Fitten et al., 1990; Schmand, Gowenberg, Smit, & Jonker, 1999; Vellinga, Smit, van Leeuwen, van Tilburg, & Jonker, 2004). The content of these instruments is further described in Appendix B. Some of these instruments use a standardized vignette, others provide semi-structured interview questions.

As shown in the table, the inter-rater reliability is fair to good, however, test-retest and internal consistency reliability have rarely been studied, and normative data are scant. Validity has been studied by comparing scores obtained on these capacity instruments with ratings by clinicians, experts, and scores on neuropsychological tests. However, most validity studies are based in relatively small samples with limited replication. Not all of the instruments are available for clinicians to use.

Summary of Psychometric Data Available for Consent Capacity Instruments

Name of Instrument	Abilities	Inter-rater Reliability	Test-Retest Reliability	Internal Consist. Reliability	Norms N
Aid to Capacity Evaluation (Etchells et al., 1999)	UAR	.93	**	**	**
Assessment of the Capacity to Consent to Treatment (Moye et al., 2008)	UARC	.90	**	.96	19
Capacity Assessment Tool (Carney, Neugroschl, Morrison, Marin, & Siu, 2001)	URC	**	**	**	**
Competency to Consent to Treatment Instrument (Marson et al., 1995)	UARC	.83-.96	**	**	15
Competency Interview Schedule (Bean, Nishiasato, Rector, & Glancy, 1994)	UARC	.95	.79	.96	**
Decision-making Assessment Measure (Wong et al., 2000)	URC	K=.87	**	**	20
Hopemont Capacity Assessment Interview (Staats et al., 1995)	UARC	.93	.29	**	**
MacCarthur Competence Assessment Tool T (Grisso & Appelbaum, 1998)	UARC	.59-.99	**	**	40
Structured Interview for Competency (Tomoda et al., 1997)	UARC	K≥ .60	**	**	**
** No information identified. U=Understanding, R=Reasoning, A=Appreciation, C=Communicating a Choice The MacCAT-T was based on three precursor instruments.					

The use of these instruments offers a standardized manner to assess each consent ability (although not all assess all four abilities), with fair to good inter-rater reliability. However, given the limited data on other psychometric properties (e.g., well-developed norms for older adults with adequate representation across sub-groups) some clinicians will find these do not meet the Daubert standard of scientific admissibility.

Nevertheless, the alternative is to use a more subjective interview, which in comparison would likely have reduced reliability relative to the more standardized approaches of these instruments. In selecting an instrument for capacity assessment of older adults, clinicians will want to consider if the instrument was developed for an older population, and for a relevant treatment situation (e.g., the CIS was developed for electroconvulsive therapy; the HCAI was developed in a long-term care setting).

Clinical Interview

As a general approach, to assess the ability to state a choice, the clinician might ask: "Have you decided whether to go along with your doctor's suggestions for treatment? Can you tell me what your decision is?"

To assess the ability to understand diagnostic and treatment information, the clinician could say: "Tell me in your own words what your understanding is of the nature of your condition, the recommended treatments, the benefits and risk of those treatments? How likely are the benefits and risks to occur?"

To assess the ability to appreciate the diagnosis and the possibility that treatments could be beneficial, a possible set of questions is "What do you really believe is wrong with your health? Do you believe that you need some kind of treatment? What is the treatment likely to do for you? What do you believe will happen if you are not treated? Do you believe the doctor is trying to harm you?"

Finally, to evaluate the ability to reason about treatment risks and benefits, the clinician could ask: "What factors were important to you in reaching the decision? How did you balance those factors? Why does Treatment A seem better than Treatment B? How will this treatment affect the things or people who are important to you?"

Values Tools are listed in **Appendix E.**

When considering values related to medical treatment, there are a number of existing tools available, such as the Values History (Doukas & McCullough, 1991). One set of questions from the Values Discussion Guide (Karel, Powell, & Cantor, 2004) is:

1. First, think about what is most important to you in your life. What makes life meaningful or good for you now?
2. Now, think about what is important to you in relation to your health. What, if any, religious or personal beliefs do you have about sickness, health care decision-making, or dying?
3. Have you or other people you know faced difficult medical treatment decisions during times of serious illness?
4. How did you feel about those situations and any choices that were made?
5. Some people feel a time might come when their life would no longer be worth living. Can you imagine any circumstances in which life would be so unbearable for you that you would not want medical treatments used to keep you alive?
6. If your spokesperson ever has to make a medical decision on your behalf, are there certain people you would want your spokesperson to talk to for advice or support (family members, friends, health care providers, clergy, other)?
7. Is there anyone you specifically would NOT want involved in helping to make health care decisions on your behalf?
8. How closely would you want your spokesperson to follow your instructions about care decisions, versus do what they think is best for you at the time decisions are made?
9. Should financial or other family concerns enter into decisions about your medical care? Please explain.
10. Are there other things you would like your spokesperson to know about you, if he or she were ever in a position to make medical treatment decisions on your behalf?

Thus, a full psychological evaluation, including a clinical interview, cognitive testing, psychodiagnostic assessment, can be combined with a capacity-specific assessment of medical consent capacity, as well as a values assessment focusing on those values most relevant to healthcare decision making. The following example describes such an approach.

Case Example

Psychological Evaluation: Medical Consent Capacity

Mr. Savin is an 81-year-old male patient referred for a psychological evaluation to determine his decisional capacity to make medical decisions for himself. The patient's medical situation recently has become more fragile and the treatment team is concerned that patient may need a medical procedure performed in the near future. The treatment team reports he has been fairly compliant with treatment, but appears to have a limited ability to understand treatment information. His answers to questions by the staff are at times odd, raising their concerns further.

Informed Consent

Mr. Savin was explained the purpose of the evaluation and that the results may be used to assist in the team's assessment of his ability to make medical decisions independently. He was warned that the capacity evaluation may result in the appointment of another person to make decisions for him. He appeared to understand the purpose, risk, and benefits of the assessment and consented to the evaluation.

Social History

Mr. Savin reported that he was raised in a local community, one of seven children. He described a positive upbringing with a close-knit family. He was raised in the Catholic religion, which he continues to practice. He reported that he advanced through school without difficulty, receiving average grades, leaving school in the 10th grade for work. He served in the Navy in the post-WWII period.

He subsequently returned home and worked for several years as a laborer. However, he has not worked since the mid-1950s due to psychiatric illness. He was never married and does not have children. He has contact with two brothers, but is generally not close to family or friends.

Mr. Savin was psychiatrically hospitalized in the mid 1950s for the first time in a state psychiatric facility, where he states he received "insulin treatments." He was subsequently psychiatrically hospitalized at the state psychiatric hospital at least four times. He has received ECT treatments in the past. After several long-term stays in the state psychiatric hospital, he eventually was placed in a psychiatric group home, where he has remained for the past 28 years.

Medical History

Mr. Savin was most recently medically hospitalized for shortness of breath and dehydration. He was subsequently transferred to a rehabilitation unit for rehabilitative therapy prior to a planned discharge most likely to a more supervised environment, such as a nursing home, due to his medical frailty.

Mr. Savin has a previous diagnosis of schizophrenia (age of onset approximately 30), cardiac disease, anemia, and gastro-esophgeal reflux disease. He is status-post multiple mycardial infarction with severe systolic function, status-post coronary artery bypass graft and mitral valve annuloplasty in 11/05, and has hyperlipidemia, hypertension, and congestive heart failure. There is no brain imaging on file.

Current Medications

Medication	Dosage/ Route/ Schedule	Indication
Epoetin Alfa Recombinant Inj	40000 UNT/1ml SC	Anemia
Ferrous Sulfate	325mg tab PO TID	Anemia
Furosemide PO	40mg tab PO QAM	Congestive Heart Failure
Lisinopril	2.5mg tab PO Q Daily	Congestive Heart Failure
Multivitamins	1 tablet PO Q Daily	Supplement to diet
Nitroglycerin SL	Sublingual 0.4mg tab Q5MIN PRN	Chest Pain

Omeprazole Cap	20mg SA PO Daily 30min prior to eating	Gerd
Risperidone	1mg tab PO QHS	Schizophrenia
Simvastatin	20mg tab PO QHS	Hypercholesterol

Clinical Interview, Including Psychiatric/Emotional Factors and Values

Mr. Savin was casually dressed with fair hygiene, demonstrated good eye contact, relatively bright affect, and good interpersonal engagement. Upon initial contact, he was sitting in front of the nurses' station with a blanket over his head. When approached, Mr. Savin removed the blanket and was pleasant, cooperative, and willing to meet with this writer. When asked why he had the blanket on his head, the patient first replied with "it's for mathematical purposes." Upon further inquiry, the patient indicated that he did not feel secure without it over him. He did not report believing someone was out to hurt him, but instead suggested it offered him a feeling of security.

His mood appeared normal and affect was mildly restricted. His speech was normal in tone and rate. He said he was not hearing voices, does not feel that he is controlled by others, reported no unusual or disturbing thoughts, and had no indication of suicidal or homicidal ideas.

Regarding values, Mr. Savin indicated that while he liked it at the rehabilitation hospital, he wished to return to his foster home. He said that he is not interested in completing advance directives and instead wants the "doctors to decide." He stated that if they could not decide, he would like the manager of his group home, whom he calls his foster mother, to decide. He stated that currently she makes financial decisions for him.

Testing

Mr. Savin was assessed with a standardized interview for consent capacity, the MacCAT-T, and a standardized neuropsychological battery. Because there was not a specific current medical treatment facing the patient, the capacity assessment interview was adapted to assess his understanding, appreciation, and reasoning of his cardiac illnesses. He displayed a high level of motivation throughout the assessment and adequate verbal comprehension. Results of this testing are judged to be a valid indicator of his current abilities.

Functional Assessment

Understanding. Mr. Savin was able to demonstrate a general knowledge of his cardiac condition, although there was also evidence of some degree of impairment. He was able to report on his cardiovascular issues and could describe in general the procedures when surgery is involved (i.e., patient is anesthetized, incisions are made, etc). When current diagnostic conditions and related treatments were described to him, he paraphrased this information back to the examiner.

Appreciation. When asked whether he had any doubts about his medical conditions, he described many of his problems as "psychosomatic." When queried, Mr. Savin reported that he needed to "concentrate and endure that responsibility on the sickness itself." He was impaired in his acknowledgement of medical conditions and the benefits of treatment. For example, when asked why someone would need additional oxygen provided to him or her (as he does) the patient responded, "You tell me . . . I react to breathing." Overall, Mr. Savin could identify a number of his cardiac issues, but had a tendency to minimize the personal significance of the conditions and the benefits of treatments.

Reasoning. When asked to describe the risks and benefits of his medications for cardiac illness and his cardiac surgeries he had difficulty. He had difficulty identifying the risks and benefits of surgery and instead deferred to his psychiatrist. For example, Mr. Savin indicated "there would be no risks or complications if Dr. X. said to do it." Mr. Savin had difficulty comparing two ideas when presented to him and could not weigh two treatment ideas. His reasoning tended to be very vague and moralistic. Oftentimes when queried to clarify his answers, he responded with "it's a mathematical purpose," and "it's a better deduction for myself personally." Thus, it was very difficult for him to justify his reasoning adequately as to why he would prefer not to have certain procedures performed.

Expressing a Choice. When asked to describe his choices for managing his cardiac illness he repeatedly deferred to his psychiatrist. He further reported that the best way a patient can help himself is to "fully cooperate with whatever the doctor says to do." When the potential serious risks of his cardiac illness and importance of his treatments were reviewed, Mr. Savin kept referring to a specific psychiatrist stating "whatever he says or who he appoints . . . I would do that."

Cognitive Assessment

Ability	Tests	%ile	Range
Attention	Digit Span & Coding	9%	Low Average
Visuospatial	Figure Copy & Line Orientation	<1%	Severely Impaired
Language	Picture Naming & Semantic Fluency	9%	Low Average
Immediate Memory	List Learning & Story Learning	5%	Moderately Impaired
Delayed Memory	List Recall/ Recognition, Story Recall & Figure Recall	21%	Low Average

On the Repeatable Battery of Neuropsychological Assessment Skills, as shown in the table, Mr. Savin had moderate impairment in immediate memory and severe impairment in visual spatial abilities. Attention, language, and delayed memory were in the low average range. Additional executive testing found moderate impairment on Trails B, and moderate difficulty on the clock drawing task.

Summary

Mr. Savin is an 81-year-old male with a history of multiple psychiatric and medical problems.
I.   Schizophrenia
II.   None
III. Cardiac illnesses
IV.   Housing problems, limited social support
V.   GAF current = 45

Based on a clinical interview, standardized capacity assessment, and cognitive testing, the following conclusions are offered:

Decision-making Capacity. Regarding his capacity to make medical decisions, it is the opinion of this clinician that this patient lacks the capacity to make medical decisions due to his psychiatric condition and general cognitive dysfunction. In terms of legal standards for medical decision making, he has a general understanding of medical information, but there is some degree of impairment that may prevent him from truly understanding the risks and benefits involved. He has trouble appreciating risks and benefits, defers to doctors excessively, and has trouble reasoning about risks and benefits because he is unable to compare two ideas. He was willing to comply with the wishes of particular doctors regardless of the risks involved. His reasoning is vague and moralistic. Mr. Savin clearly states on several occasions that he does not like to make important decisions and while he feels he is able to do so, he prefers others to make them for him. He was unable to express a specific treatment preference. While it is the opinion of this clinician that the patient could consent to very low-risk medical procedures (i.e., having blood drawn), he lacks the capacity to provide consent independently to procedures where there are potentially more serious risks, and the complexity of the information is greater.

Cognitive Functioning. Regarding his cognition, he has adequate simple attention and memory after a delay, but his working memory, visual spatial skills, and executive function are moderately to severely impaired. He appears to have difficulty organizing verbal and visual information and becomes quickly overwhelmed.

He has difficulty switching between two concepts. These deficits are consistent with his long-standing diagnosis of schizophrenia.

Recommendations

1. Substitute decision maker. Based on the results of this interview, it is recommended that the treatment team work with Mr. Savin to identify a possible healthcare proxy. He has limited contact with his brothers, and they may be appropriate to serve in this role. Otherwise, it may be possible to appoint a DPA or limited guardian for medical decisions.
2. Dementia evaluation. Mr. Savin displays cognitive deficits consistent with schizophrenia. Nevertheless, he has many cardiac risk factors for vascular dementia. The team may wish to consider a full medical evaluation for dementia and possible reversible causes of cognitive impairment.
3. Financial capacity. Although it was not the focus of this evaluation, results of the patient interview and cognitive testing suggest that Mr. Savin may have difficulty managing his finances. According to the patient, his psychiatric group home manager has assisted with his finances. Given that he is no longer living at the group home, and it is uncertain that he will return, it may be appropriate to explore if this arrangement should continue, be formalized, or if another fiduciary should be identified.
4. Presentation of information. Given Mr. Savin's tendency to become overwhelmed by information, it will be important to provide information about medical decisions in simple, structured manner, limiting the amount of information provided at any one time.
5. Given Mr. Savin's complex medical problems and prognosis, it is important to facilitate a discussion with him and possibly family members to facilitate an understanding of Mr. Savin's preferences and values regarding advanced illness interventions.
6. Ongoing assessment and treatment of his psychiatric symptoms is recommended.

Sexual Consent Capacity

Introduction

Under American law, all individuals who have reached the age of consent have the right, and are assumed to have the capacity, to consent to sexual relations. The age of consent varies across states from 16 to 18 years of age. The nature of sexual behaviors requiring consent can range from touching to sexual intercourse. Long-term care facilities tend to be the primary venue for the issue of sexual consent capacity to be questioned. Sexual behavior between long-term care residents is a complicated issue that can create a tension between the desire of staff and family members to protect potentially vulnerable residents, and the desire of residents to meet their sexual needs and assert their rights to sexual relations. Long-term care staff are particularly concerned with the diminished capacity of residents to consent to sexual relations (Lichtenberg & Strezepek, 1990) and the propriety of resident sexual behavior (Wallace, 2003).

Consent is the cardinal element in the determination of the legality of sexual relations (Stavis, 1991). Constitutional, civil, and criminal law can each have relevance to the sexual activities of long-term care residents (Stavis, 1991). Long-term care facilities, which are licensed by their states, have a legal obligation (state and constitutional) to protect its residents from unreasonable harm (Lyden, 2007). There is considerable variability in the statutory definitions of capacity to consent to sexual activity, ranging from very conservative to very liberal tests (Lyden, 2007; Stavis & Walker-Hirsch, 1999; Sundram & Stavis, 1993).

Unique aspects of sexual consent capacity differentiate it from other forms of consent capacity (Kennedy, 1999). For example, an individual facing a medical treatment decision is given information upon which a decision is to be made. There are opportunities for one to discuss this information with others and obtain advice from one's physician and significant others. There are often opportunities to weigh the risks and benefits of decisions with other individuals. In contrast, the individual facing a decision regarding sexual activities is often alone, with the exception of the sexual partner(s), often without the opportunity, or desire, to consult with others, and in a situation that often requires a relatively rapid response. Finally, there can be no surrogate decision maker for sexual relations. Considerably more attention has been paid to the issue of sexual consent among intellectually disabled individuals in both the legal and clinical literatures, than to cognitively impaired older adults. Kennedy (1999) has argued that the sexual consent capacity standards applied to individuals with intellectual or developmental disabilities are applicable to individuals with dementia. This literature may provide additional information for the reader.

Legal Standard

There are no universally accepted criteria for capacity to consent to sexual relations (Lyden, 2007). The legal standards and criteria for sexual consent vary across states (Lyden, 2007; Stavis et al., 1999). The most widely accepted criteria, which are consistent with those applied to consent to treatment, are: (1) *knowledge* of relevant information, including risks and benefits; (2) *understanding* or rational reasoning that reveals a decision that is consistent with the individual's values (competence); and (3) *voluntariness* (a stated choice without coercion) (Grisso, 2003; Kennedy, 1999; Stavis, 1991; Stavis et al., 1999; Sundram et al., 1993). In light of the variation in standards across jurisdictions, the reader is encouraged to read relevant state law.

Functional Elements

Sexual consent is a complicated construct, with knowledge, capacity, and voluntariness, intertwined.

1. Knowledge

This criterion requires that an individual be able to demonstrate a basic knowledge of the sexual activities in question, potential risks (e.g., pregnancy, sexually transmitted diseases) and how to prevent them, the responsibilities of pregnancy and parenthood, illegal sexual activities (e.g., sexual assault, coercion, sexual activities with incapacitated individuals, sexual activities with under-age individuals), how to determine whether sexual activities are not desired by the partner, and appropriate times and places for sexual activities. Several sexual knowledge surveys that may be of use to the clinician are listed by Lyden (2007).

2. Capacity

This criterion comprises the abilities of decision-making capacity (Appelbaum et al., 1988; Roth et al., 1977). They include the ability to understand the options related to the sexual behavior, appreciate the consequences of various courses of action, and express a choice that is based on a rational or logical consideration of relevant knowledge, including the personal benefits and risks of the sexual activity, and is consistent with the individual's values and preferences.

3. Voluntariness

This criterion requires that an individual have the ability to make a decision regarding sexual activity that does not result from coercion, unfair persuasion, or inducements (Lyden, 2007; Moye, 2003). There are differences across jurisdictions regarding what constitutes illegal influence (Wertheimer, 2003).

Diagnostic Considerations

With the exception of mental retardation (Kennedy & Niederbuhl, 2001), sexual consent capacity has not been studied in relation to the various diagnostic categories. Though individuals with intellectual or developmental disabilities may share cognitive deficits with individuals with dementia, the literatures are distinct and have not yet been integrated. One might presume that because sexual consent shares many of the functional elements of medical consent, and likely requires many of the same cognitive skills, that the literature on the effects of various psychiatric disorders on medical consent could inform the judgment of the clinician who is evaluating an individual for

sexual consent. For example, one might presume that dementia or schizophrenia could diminish capacity. Knowledge and voluntariness, which are both important functional elements for assessment, are less likely to be considered by the clinician evaluating an individual for medical consent. Thus, the parallel between medical and sexual consent is not complete.

Cognitive Underpinnings

Though some empirical findings may inform us about some of the cognitive skills required for each of the three for sexual consent capacity criteria, there is virtually no research evidence that bears directly on the cognitive elements of each of these criteria as they pertain to sexual activities among older adults in long-term care facilities. One would expect some of the cognitive abilities required for the capacity to consent to medical treatment to be relevant for sexual consent capacity, particularly for the elements of knowledge and understanding. In light of the lack of empirical evidence, possible abilities required for sexual consent capacity are offered:

1. Cognitive Functions Related to Knowledge

Possible cognitive abilities include attention, semantic memory for basic biological information regarding conception, pregnancy, sexually transmitted diseases, methods of preventing risks, social mores concerning sexual behavior, and illegal sexual activities. Autobiographical/episodic memory and higher order cognitive abilities (e.g., executive function) might be required to appreciate the motives of a potential partner. Procedural memory is necessary for utilizing devices for the prevention of pregnancy and the spread of sexually transmitted diseases.

2. Cognitive Functions Related to Capacity

Possible cognitive abilities include attention, verbal comprehension of information presented by a potential partner, semantic memory for presented information, historical information that pertains to the current situation, and information pertaining to the risks and benefits of various sexual activities. These abilities also may include abstraction and executive functions required for the logical or rational consideration of the benefits and risks of the sexual activity, episodic memory for related experiences, personal values, and preferences. Finally, the ability to express a choice has been related to auditory and confrontation naming, as indicated in the preceding medical consent section.

3. Cognitive Functions Related to Voluntariness

Possible cognitive abilities include attention, abstraction, and executive functions for the consideration of factors that could imply coercion, unfair persuasion, or inappropriate inducements. Semantic and episodic memory may be required for contrasting the current circumstances with those previously experienced (directly or indirectly).

Psychiatric and Emotional Factors

As with the diagnostic factors, there is little literature to offer guidance here. The cognitive abilities that are likely required for sexual consent are considerable. The complex ability to weigh risks and benefits of sexual behavior is perhaps the most vulnerable of the abilities. Moderate to severe symptoms of depression and anxiety could impact this ability. Sexual and romantic relationships also bring their own set of strong, potentially "troublesome," emotions that could interfere with the ability to rationally weigh risks and benefits associated with sexual behavior. Moreover, these emotions can leave one more vulnerable to exploitation by a potential partner. Fear of abandonment and loneliness can also leave one more vulnerable.

Values

Community-dwelling older adults continue to value and enjoy sexual relationships throughout their lives (Masters & Johnson, 1966; Janus & Janus, 1993; Mathias, Lubben, Atchison, & Schweitzer, 1997). This is the case for nursing home residents as well (Lantz, 2004; Richardson, 1995). Though sexual attitudes of the general population about sexual expression of older adults have moved in a positive direction over the years, lesbian/gay/bisexual/transgendered (LGBT) older adults face unique legal and social issues in general, and regarding their decision-making rights in particular. In addition, the importance of sexuality likely varies between individuals, as well as sexual expression. One should not expect unique gender role differences and family structures to always be well understood by staff members, some of whom may also not share attitudes with the older adults. A recent MetLife study revealed that a substantial percentage of LGBT baby boomers are concerned about discrimination as they age and are concerned that they will not be treated with dignity and respect by healthcare professionals.

Staff members of long-term care facilities do not always place a high value on resident personal choice for a variety of reasons, sometimes this is for the sake of expedience, and sometimes it is due to conflicting personal values. In the latter case, sexual expression among residents may not always be at the top of the list of staff preferred resident behaviors. Though many staff members believe that residents have sexual needs, considerably fewer believe that older adult resident discussions of sexuality or maintaining an attractive self-image are important (Lantz, 2004). Even the children of older adult residents often oppose sexual contact between their parents and other residents (Lichtenberg et al., 1990).

Clinicians should consider their own level of comfort in broaching topics related to sexuality, their attitudes toward sexuality among older adults, and the stereotypes and myths that might influence their attitudes and comfort level.

Risks

The intimacy and sexual needs of long-term care residents present a challenge to facility staff, who must balance the risks of sexual activity with the individual right to autonomy, and the values, preferences, and sexual needs of its residents. There can be personal risks for the individual desiring sexual activity, and risks for residents without sexual consent capacity. Risks to the resident include, for example, exploitation, psychological or physical abuse, sexually transmitted disease, pregnancy, social rejection by staff or other residents, and even harassment by family members of the sexual partner. Risks for the facility can be considerable, as a facility has the responsibility of protecting its residents from unreasonable harm resulting from sexual activity.

Rather than considering a single threshold for consent capacity, sexual consent may be best approached with attention to capacity for decisions regarding particular types of sexual activities. These could range, for example, from kissing to sexual intercourse.

Steps to Enhance Capacity

Most of the abilities required for demonstrating sexual consent capacity are cognitive in nature. Sex education materials can be provided when deficits in knowledge are identified. Assistive devices can be provided for sensory deficits and physical disabilities. Depending upon the nature of memory deficits, memory aids can be created. Problem solving skills can be taught to augment an individual's ability to identify potential inappropriate or coercive situations, generate effective approaches to addressing these situations, and methods for selecting among the alternatives generated. Rules of thumb, or heuristics, could be taught for avoiding or escaping such situations.

Clinical Judgment of Sexual Consent Capacity

Sexual behavior varies along several dimensions, including risk to the individual. Thus, the determination of capacity need not require a binary judgment. One should consider clinical judgments that include outcomes that vary along a dimension of potential risk to the resident and the partner. Recommendations can be made that would permit varying levels of sexual contact, intimacy, and risk.

This judgment incorporates a particularly complex set of interactive factors that include knowledge and voluntariness, and numerous other related historical and current factors noted above. These factors, and the foundation abilities of capacity, must all be integrated to yield a judgment that balances the protection of

the resident, partner, and institution. Information obtained from the interview of the resident, staff members, and perhaps the potential partner, is the most externally valid information available given the typical circumstances. Cognitive assessment can certainly inform and support one's conclusions, but ultimately one must be convinced that the resident is capable of acting with capacity in the moment. The more functional the assessment, the more confident one is likely to be with the final judgment.

Clinical Approaches to Assessing Sexual Consent Capacity

The clinical assessment of consent capacity is unlikely to receive judicial review unless the case involves litigation (Moye at al., 2007). A typical case might involve two nursing home residents desiring sexual activities, with at least one of the residents having questionable capacity. Concern regarding vulnerability of one of the residents could be expressed by staff and/or family members, which leads to a request to assess a resident regarding sexual consent capacity. Another typical case might involve a less cognitively impaired male approaching a cognitively impaired women, with an attempt to initiate sexual contact (Lichtenberg, 2007). Long-term care staff may argue that the individuals have a special relationship, only to learn later that an impaired woman who had been approached by a cognitively impaired man thought that the man was her husband (Lichtenberg, 2007). A third problem arises when staff enter into sexual relations with residents, which is clearly inappropriate and should be addressed by facility policies. Finally, as noted above, sexuality exists on a continuum, ranging from hand holding or touching to sexual intercourse. Preliminary information gathering might include a review of resident records regarding (reproductive ability, history of sexual activity in the facility (including information regarding past inappropriate or coerced activities), evidence that the resident might be vulnerable to undue influence or coercion, cognitive functioning, and disorders that could impair cognitive functioning or limit or increase sexual activity. Discussions with staff, and family where relevant, regarding cognitive, behavioral, and emotional functioning can be helpful. Finally, formal assessment of the resident's cognitive and functional abilities should be conducted. A staff member with whom the resident feels comfortable (e.g., same gender, personally familiar) might be enlisted to explain the purpose and process of the assessment (Lyden, 2007). The staff member could remain for the assessment if the resident feels more comfortable with that arrangement.

There are no generally accepted approaches or criteria for the assessment of consent to sexual activity. Stavis et al., (1999) suggest that the following be considered by the examining clinician, with the understanding that some individuals with capacity to consent would not meet all of these criteria:

Is an adult, as defined by state law; demonstrates an awareness of person, time, place, and event; possesses a basic knowledge of sexual activities; possesses the skills to participate safely in sexual activities; i.e., whether the person understands how and why to effectively use an appropriate method of birth control, and whether the person chooses to do so; understands the physical and legal responsibilities of pregnancy; is aware of sexually transmittable diseases and how to avoid them; demonstrates an awareness of legal implications concerning wrongful sexual behaviors (e.g., sexual assault, inappropriateness of sex with minors, exploitation, etc.); can identify when others rights are infringed; learns that no from another person means to stop (i.e., understands that it is always inappropriate to have sex or engage in other activities with someone who says no or otherwise objects by words or action)s; knows when sexual advances are appropriate as to time and place (e.g., different places and times may apply to dancing, touching, sexual intercourse); does not allow his or her own disability to be exploited by a partner; knows when both parties are agreeing to the same sexual activity; does not exploit another person with a lower functioning who might not be able to say no or defend oneself; expresses understandable responses to life

experiences (i.e., can accurately report events); can describe the decision-making process used to make the choice to engage in sexual activity; demonstrates the ability to differentiate truth from fantasy and lies; possesses a reasoning process that includes an expression of individual values; can reasonably execute choices associated with a judgmental process; is able to identify and recognize the feelings expressed by others, both verbally and nonverbally; expresses emotions consistent with the actual or proposed sexual situation; rejects unwanted advances or intrusions to protect oneself from sexual exploitation; identifies and uses private areas for intimate behavior; is able to call for help or report unwanted advances or abuse (Stavis et al., 1999, p. 63-64).

Peter Lichtenberg offers the following suggestions for assessing sexual consent capacity:

1. *Patient s awareness of the relationship:*
    a. *Is the patient aware of who is initiating sexual contact?*
    b. *Does the patient believe that the other person is a spouse and, thus, acquiesces out of a delusional belief, or [is he/she] cognizant of the other s identity and intent?*
    c. *Can the patient state what level of sexual intimacy [he/she] would be comfortable with?*
2. *Patient s ability to avoid exploitation:*
    a. *Is the behavior consistent with formerly held beliefs/values?*
    b. *Does the patient have the capacity to say no to any uninvited sexual contact?*
3. *Patient s awareness of potential risks:*
    a. *Does the patient realize that this relationship may be time limited (placement on unit is temporary)?*
    b. *Can the patient describe how [he/she] will react when the relationship ends?*

These authors note that while being able to state the level of sexual activity or intimacy is wanted is an important consideration, one must also assess the ability to refuse or resist sexual advances. Lichtenberg et al., also emphasized the importance of residents understanding that the ending of a relationship might be one of the potential risks of entering in to a sexual relationship. Residents can leave facilities for a variety of reasons (e.g., transfer due to illness), thereby terminating the relationship.

Long-term care facilities should have policies and procedures regarding sexual relations that are consistent with state statutes, and staff should receive in-service training to develop a sensitivity to this issue (Lichtenberg, 2007). See the following for examples of an institutional policy: www.hebrewhome.org/se.asp or Center for Practical Bioethics (2006). Psychologists are encouraged to become familiar with the U.S. Code of Federal Regulations (42 CFR Part 483), which discusses the requirements for states and long term care facilities. In particular, the sections on resident rights (483.10), resident behavior and facility practices (483.13), quality of life (483.15), and resident assessment (483.20) are relevant to the sexual behavior of individual residents. These regulations can be found at http://www.access.gpo.gov/nara/cfr/waisidx_03/42cfr483_03.html

Functional Assessment Instruments

There are no standardized instruments to assess sexual consent capacity.

Case Example

Psychological Evaluation: Consent to Sexual Activity

Ms. Smith is a 64-year-old woman living in a nursing facility, who was referred for a routine psychological evaluation and determination of capacity to consent to sexual activity. The resident desires a sexual relationship with another resident, whom staff believe is mistreating Ms. Smith. The staff is concerned that Ms. Smith does not recall these episodes of mistreatment and is concerned about her ability to consent to sexual activities.

Informed Consent

The purpose of the capacity evaluation was explained to Ms. Smith. The concern of staff members was conveyed to Ms. Smith, as was the

possible consequence of finding her lacking capacity to consent to sexual activity. She indicated that she understood the rationale for the evaluation and appreciated the staff's concern for her well-being. She felt confident that she would be found to have capacity, but admitted that her memory was oftentimes poor.

Social History

Ms. Smith attended school through the 10th grade and worked as a saleswoman. She was married three times and has one son by her second marriage. Ms. Smith was in an automobile accident about 20 years ago, resulting in traumatic brain injury. No documentation of the injury is contained in her records.

Medical History

Ms. Smith's records reveal a history of depression, for which she was hospitalized several years ago and was treated successfully with an antidepressant. She has a history of seizures dating back to her accident, although her records indicate that they have been completely controlled by medication. Ms. Smith was transferred to the present facility one year ago from another nursing facility where her behavior became unmanageable. The major complaint of staff at the other facility was verbal outbursts and accusations made at staff. Since arriving at the present facility she has adjusted reasonably well and made several friends, including the man with whom she has become romantically involved. Her outbursts were initially limited to times at which she wished to be taken to the bathroom, and resulted when staff did not comply immediately with her requests. These outbursts were virtually eliminated with a behavior management plan implemented by nursing staff. Ms. Smith is ambulatory with a wheelchair and is unable to walk unassisted. She requires assistance with activities of daily living. Ms. Smith complains frequently of pain and requests pain medication, in spite of the fact that she is receiving what should be adequate pain medication. Ms. Smith argues that the dosage is incorrect and insufficient, and states that she was given larger amounts of pain medication at the facility from which she was transferred. Ms. Smith also complains of discomfort in her stomach, which may be due to dilation of her bowel duct and which will likely be corrected with minor surgery. She requests frequently that she be taken to the bathroom to urinate. Medical causes of the reported frequent need to urinate have been ruled out. Staff members report that on many occasions, Ms. Smith fails to urinate when taken to the bathroom. Nevertheless, she is receiving medication for an overactive bladder.

Ms. Smith's current ICD diagnoses are Essential Hypertension, Osteoporosis, Chronic Airway Obstruction NEC, Epilepsy, and Depressive Disorder NEC. No brain imaging records are in her chart.
Staff interview:

Staff Interview

Nursing staff were interviewed about their concerns regarding "mistreatment." They reported that they occasionally observed acts of jealousy by Ms. Smith's partner when she attended to another male, and which was followed by his grabbing her by the arm and firmly telling her to stay away from the other resident. The staff did not observe any verbal, physical, or sexual abuse. Their concerns were limited to a question of whether Mrs. Smith had the capacity to engage in the sexual relationship in the context of her known cognitive deficits.

Current Medications

Medication	Dosage/Route/Schedule	Indication
Acetaminophen	2325mg tabs PRN po Q4hrs	Pain
Acetaminophen with Codeine	300mg tab pot id	Pain
Aspirin	325mg tab po qd	Hypertension
Carbamazepine	3100mg tabs po bid	Seizures
Carbamazepine	200mg tab po qd	Seizures
Valsartan	80 mg tab po qd	Hypertension

Gabapentin	600mg tab po tid	Pain
Ibuprofen	400mg pot id	Pain
Pirbuterol	0.2mg 2 puffs po qid	COPD
Mirtazapine	30mg tab po hs	Depression
Oxybutynin	5mg tab po qd	Overactive Bladder
Phenobarbital	60mg tab po bid	Convulsions

Clinical Interview and Behavioral Observations

Ms. Smith was approached in the recreation room, where she was sitting in her wheelchair watching television. She smiled and welcomed this examiner. She was appropriately dressed in jeans, blouse, and sneakers. She spoke slowly and evidenced mild dysarthria. Her motor activity evidenced mild to moderate bradykinesia. She was oriented to person and place, but not to time, reporting an incorrect date and day of the week. Her mood was euthymic and congruent with her current affect. Ms. Smith denied suicidal and homicidal ideation, delusions, and hallucinations. She denied problems with sleeping and appetite. Ms. Smith failed to state the correct reason that she was in the hospital, indicating that she thought she was here to check on her "bad temper." She appeared to be attentive and motivated throughout the evaluation period.

Review of Medications

Ms. Smith's medications were reviewed to determine whether any could substantially affect any of the cognitive skills that are considered relevant for sexual consent capacity. Memory was considered the most important of these in light of Ms. Smith's cognitive assessment results. A review of her medications revealed only one, carbamazepine, that might be contributing substantially to memory impairment. However, the effects on memory and fatigue typically pass over time. Valsartan, her anti-hypertensive medication, can actually improve word list recall. Ms. Smith had been receiving this medication for several years.

Functional Capacity Assessment

Ms. Smith demonstrated satisfactory knowledge of sexual activities, including intercourse, understanding of the potential risks and benefits of sexual behavior, and the appropriate times and places for such behavior. She demonstrated an understanding of how condoms are used to prevent the spread of sexually transmitted diseases and an understanding of how they could be obtained by her and properly used. Ms. Smith understood the need for privacy for most forms of sexual expression, and the fact that some staff members were uncomfortable with public displays of affection among residents. Ms. Smith understood that she always has a choice of whether to engage in sexual behavior and that such behavior should be consistent with her values and preferences. She demonstrated an understanding that sexual behavior should be free of coercion, unfair persuasion, or any inducements by her or her partner. The question of how Ms. Smith would weigh the benefits of sexual behavior against the potential inappropriate behavior (e.g., occasional yelling, arm grabbing) of her partner, often due to jealousy, was discussed. She expressed some concern that her partner could become more aggressive and indicated that if he did, she would terminate the relationship. This response must be considered in light of Ms. Smith reporting that having a relationship with a man was very important to her, and that she did not feel she had many suitable men from which to choose in the facility. Several potential scenarios were presented to Ms. Smith to determine how she would consider the elements of potential situations that could involve sexual behavior, weigh the risks and benefits in light of her values, and make choices that were consistent with these considerations.

Cognitive Assessment

Attention was assessed through an examination of digit span forward from the WAIS-III and the Attention subscale of the Cognistat. Ms. Smith correctly repeated 7 digits forward, which is .44 standard deviations above the mean of 6.35 for adults ages 55-64. Ms. Smith earned a score of 8 on the Cognistat subscale, which is almost one standard deviation above the mean for healthy adults of approximately her age.

Memory was assessed with the Memory subscale of the Cognistat and the Hopkins Verbal Learning Test - Revised (HVLT-R). Ms. Smith obtained a score of 4 on the Cognistat Memory subscale, which is 10.7 standard deviations below the mean of 11.5 for adults of comparable age. The HVLT-R is a test of verbal learning and short-term memory. Ms. Smith recalled none of the initial 12 words following a 20-minute delay. Her total score of 21 is 1.5 standard deviations below the norm of 27.5 (sd=4.3) for healthy adults.

Ms. Smith's memory for previously acquired information regarding sexually transmitted diseases and methods of preventing risks was quite good. Ms. Smith's recall of past encounters with her potential partner was problematic, as evidenced by her poor performance on a delayed recall task and her statements to staff that she did not recall her potential partner treating her badly (e.g., yelling at her, grabbing her arm) on previous days. It was unclear from these reports whether Ms. Smith was feigning poor recall so that she could justify spending time with her potential partner.

Executive Function was assessed with the Trails B, Similarities and Judgment subscales of the Cognistat, and COWAT. Ms. Smith earned a score of 5 on the Similarities subscale of the Cognistat, which is almost two standard deviations below the normative mean of 6.1. She earned a score of 5 on the Judgment subscale, which is approximately at the normative mean of 5.1. Ms. Smith named 10 unique animals on the COWAT, which is 2.3 standard deviations below the normative mean of 19.8. The poor performance on the Trails B and COWAT, both speeded tests, must be considered in light of Ms. Smith's bradykinesia.

Activities of Daily Living were assessed with the Adult Functional Adaptive Behavior Scale (AFABS) by a nurse familiar with Ms. Smith. Moderate impairment in ambulation, toileting, dressing, grooming, socialization, managing money, managing health needs, and memory were noted. Mild impairment was noted in eating, environmental orientation, reality orientation, receptive speech comprehension, and expressive communication.

Psychiatric/Emotional Assessment

Depression was assessed using the Geriatric Depression Scale- Short Form (GDS). Ms. Smith obtained a score of 2, well below the cutoff score of 5. She endorsed items regarding problems with memory and lack of energy.

Summary

Ms. Smith is a 64-year-old female with a history of depression and traumatic brain injury, who has required nursing home placement for over 20 years. The nursing facility staff are concerned that she lacks capacity to consent to sexual behavior, due primarily to her poor memory. The following conclusions are offered based on a clinical interview and psychological testing:

Ms. Smith demonstrated adequate attention, but moderate impairment in immediate memory and severe impairment in delayed memory. Remote autobiographical memory appeared adequate. Staff reports of Ms. Smith's memory for recent incidents with her potential partner suggest recent episodic memory impairment. Ms. Smith's own report of her memory performance is consistent with this observation. Depression was ruled out as a likely contributor to memory impairment through consideration of her scores on measures of depression and attention. Her current medications are also unlikely to be a major source of her memory difficulties. Ms. Smith's performance on the tests of executive function was of limited value in light of the potential influence of her bradykinesia. However, functional assessment, as noted below, revealed satisfactory reasoning, planning, and problem solving.

Functional assessment of decision-making capacity yielded evidence that she appreciated that she always had a choice of engaging in sexual behavior, that she could understand and weigh the potential risks and benefits of such behavior in light of her own values, and that she could arrive at a decision that was consistent with her reasoning and values.

Ms. Smith appears to have the knowledge and many of the functional skills necessary for making informed, well-reasoned decisions regarding sexual behavior. However, her poor delayed memory precludes her learning from past experiences. This is particularly problematic because her partner has allegedly been seen mistreating Ms. Smith, and Ms. Smith reports no recall of those episodes. Moreover, Ms. Smith reports she fears her partner could become aggressive. Since Ms. Smith cannot recall past experiences with her partner, she lacks the information that would be used to avoid future aversive or physically dangerous interactions. It is the opinion of this clinician that Ms. Smith lacks the capacity to consent to sexual behavior. There is no reason, however, that Ms. Smith and her potential partner could not visit with each other as long as the visits occur in locations where staff can monitor their behavior.

Financial Capacity

Introduction

Financial capacity is a medical-legal construct that represents the ability to independently manage one's financial affairs in a manner consistent with personal self-interest and values (Marson & Hebert, 2008a). Financial capacity, thus, involves not only performance skills (e.g., counting coins/currency accurately, completing a check register accurately, paying bills), but also judgment skills that optimize financial self-interest, and values that guide personal financial choices. Financial experience and skills can vary widely among cognitively normal individuals and are associated with factors of education and socioeconomic status.

From a legal standpoint, financial capacity represents the financial skills sufficient for handling one's estate and financial affairs, and is the basis for determinations of conservatorship of the estate (or guardianship of the estate, depending on the state legal jurisdiction). Broadly construed, financial capacity also conceptually encompasses more specific legal capacities, such as contractual capacity, donative capacity, and testamentary capacity. Thus, financial capacity is an important area of assessment in the civil legal system. (Marson et al., 2008a).

From a clinical standpoint, financial capacity is a highly cognitively mediated capacity that is vulnerable to neurological, psychiatric, and medical conditions that affect cognition (such as dementia, stroke, traumatic brain injury, and schizophrenia). In particular, financial capacity issues arise frequently in the context of older adults with cognitive loss and dementia. Family members of such older adults will often raise concerns about new problems managing household finances, making poor financial decisions, or being exploited/scammed. Clinicians are increasingly being asked by families, physicians, attorneys, and judges to evaluate and offer clinical opinions regarding financial capacity (Marson et al., 2008a).

Legal Elements/Standards

For historical reasons, Anglo-American law has traditionally treated an individual's financial capacity separately from the capacity to manage personal affairs. Conservatorship (or guardianship of the estate) is a set of legal procedures in which a court evaluates an individual's overall capacity to manage his/her financial affairs and decides whether or not to appoint a conservator to manage part or all of them instead. Conservatorships can be limited or plenary. The legal standard for conservatorship varies across state jurisdictions, and historically was often generally (vaguely) cast as the capacity to manage in a reasonable manner all of one's financial affairs.

A better and far more specific criterion is set forth in Section 410(2) of the Uniform Guardianship and Protective Proceedings Act (UGPPA), which states that a court may appoint a conservator if the court determines that "the individual is unable to manage property and business affairs because of an impairment in the ability to receive and evaluate information or make decisions, even with the use of appropriate technological assistance" and

> the individual has property that will be wasted or dissipated unless management is provided or money is needed for the support, care, education, health, and welfare of the individual or of individuals who are entitled to the individual's support and that protection is necessary or desirable to obtain or provide money. (Uniform Law Commissioners, http://www.nccusl.org/Update/)

It is important for the practicing psychologist to be familiar with the definition of financial capacity in his/her state (Marson et al., 2008a).

As discussed above, financial capacity also conceptually encompasses specific types of legal transactions, such as executing a contract (contractual capacity), making a gift (donative capacity), or making a will (testamentary capacity). The legal standard for contractual capacity is high and generally involves the party's ability *to understand the nature and effect of the act and the business being transacted* (Walsh et al., 1994; Mezzullo et al., 2002).

In contrast, for reasons of public policy, the legal standard for testamentary capacity is low. Although requirements for testamentary capacity vary across states, four criteria have been identified. A testator must know what a will is, have knowledge of his/her potential heirs, have knowledge of the nature and extent of his/her assets; and have a general plan of distribution of assets to heirs. The absence of one or more of these elements of testamentary capacity can serve as grounds for a court to invalidate a will. Testamentary capacity is treated separately, in the next section of Chapter 6.

The standard for donative capacity, or the capacity to give a gift can also vary across jurisdictions. In some states, a comprehension standard is applied similar to that used in contractual matters: *the party contemplating the donative transfer must understand the nature and effect of the act of making a gift.* In other jurisdictions, a lower standard equivalent to that of testamentary capacity is applied.

Functional Elements

Financial capacity is a complex, multi-dimensional construct representing a broad range of conceptual, pragmatic, and judgmental skills (Marson et al., 2005). Initial conceptual formulations of financial capacity were limited to unelaborated descriptions, such as "money management skills" or "financial management skills." To date, some state statutory definitions of financial capacity continue to maintain this level of vagueness. However, recent clinical studies have begun to model and empirically investigate this capacity and its constituent functional abilities.

As discussed above, in considering functional abilities relevant to financial capacity, a fundamental consideration involves the dual performance and self-interest perspectives discussed above. For example, a person with schizophrenia may have adequate financial performance skills but lack financial capacity because he/she consistently makes poor judgments about how to spend government entitlement monies.

Marson and colleagues have proposed a clinical model of financial capacity that represents an initial effort at identifying functional elements constituent to this capacity (Griffith et al., 2003; Marson et al., 2000), shown on the following page. The model focuses on both performance and judgment skills and conceptualizes financial capacity at three increasingly complex levels.

1. Specific Abilities and Tasks

The first functional element is specific financial abilities or tasks, each of which is relevant to a particular domain of financial activity. In the model, many general domains can be further broken down into component tasks or abilities that emphasize understanding and pragmatic application of skills relevant to a specific domain. For instance, the domain of financial conceptual knowledge involves understanding concepts, such as loans and savings, and also using this information to select advantageous interest rates. Similarly, bill payment involves not only understanding what a bill is and why it should be paid, but accurately reviewing a bill and preparing it for mailing.

2. General Domains

The second functional level is general domains of financial activity, each of which are clinically relevant to the independent functioning of community-dwelling older adults. In this model, core domains include basic monetary skills, financial conceptual knowledge, cash transactions, checkbook management, bank statement management, financial judgment, bill payment, knowledge of personal assets and estate arrangements, and investment decision making.

3. Overall Capacity

The third functional level is overall financial capacity, or a global level. The global level of the model considers overall financial capacity. Clinicians are usually asked by families and the courts to make clinical judgments concerning an individual's overall financial capacity. Such global judgments involve an integration of information concerning an individual's task and domain level performance, his/her judgment skills, and informant reports of financial abilities. Such global clinical judgments are particularly relevant to conservatorship hearings.

The model has informed instrument development and served as the basis for several empirical studies of financial capacity in dementia (Marson et al., 2000; Griffith et al., 2003, Martin et al., 2008).

However, these studies notwithstanding, there is not yet a clear consensus as to the

Conceptual Model of Financial Capacity:		
	Task Description	**Difficulty**
Domain 1 Basic Monetary Skills		
Task 1a Naming Coins/Currency	Identify specific coins and currency	Simple
Task 1b Coin/Currency relationships	Indicate monetary values of coins/currency	Simple
Task 1c Counting coins/currency	Accurately count arrays of coins and currency	Simple
Domain 2 Financial Conceptual Knowledge		
Task 2a Define financial concepts	Define simple financial concepts	Complex
Task 2b Apply financial concepts	Practical applications/computation using concepts	Complex
Domain 3 Cash Transactions		
Task 3a 1 item grocery purchase	Conduct 1 item transaction; verify change	Simple
Task 3b 3 item grocery purchase	Conduct 3 item transaction; verify change	Complex
Task 3c Change/vending machine	Obtain change for vending machine; verify charge	Complex
Task 3d Tipping	Understand tipping convention; calculate tips	Complex
Domain 4 Checkbook Management		
Task 4a Understand checkbook	Identify/explain parts of checkbook and register	Simple
Task 4b Use checkbook/register	Conduct simple transaction and pay by check	Complex
Domain 5 Bank Statement Management		
Task 5a Understand bank statement	Identify/explain parts of a bank statement	Complex
Task 5b Use bank statement	Identify specific transactions on bank statement	Complex
Domain 6 Financial Judgment		
Task 6a Detect mail fraud risk	Detect/explain risks in mail fraud solicitation	Simple
Task 6b Detect telephone fraud risk	Detect/explain risks in telephone fraud solicitation	Simple
Domain 7 Bill Payment		
Task 7a Understand bills	Explain meaning and purpose of bills	Simple
Task 7b Prioritize bills	Identify overdue utility bill	Simple
Task 7c Prepare bills for mailing	Prepare bills, checks, envelopes for mailing	Complex
Domain 8 Knowledge of Assets/Estate	Indicate personal assets and estate arrangements	Simple
Domain 9 Investment Decision Making	Understand investment options; determine returns; make and explain decision	Complex
Overall Financial Capacity	**Overall functioning across tasks and domains**	**Complex**

^ requires corroboration by informant
Reprinted with permission from Griffith, H.R., Belue, K., Sicola, A., Krzywanski, S., Zamrini, E., Harrell, L., & Marson, D. C. (2003). Impaired financial abilities in mild cognitive impairment: A direct assessment approach. *Neurology, 60,* 449 - 457.

functional elements that comprise financial capacity. There is a significant need for both neuropsychological and factor analytic studies to identify component constructs and functional elements for this capacity.

Diagnostic Considerations

Financial capacity is a multi-dimensional and highly cognitive mediated capacity. Accordingly, it is a capacity that is very sensitive to medical conditions that affect cognitive and behavioral functioning. Medical conditions that impair financial capacity include neurodegenerative disorders like Alzheimer's disease (AD) and Parkinson's disease, severe psychiatric disorders like schizophrenia and bipolar disorder, substance abuse disorders, and developmental disorders, such as mental retardation and autism.

Existing empirical research in this area has focused on changes in financial capacity occurring in the context of Alzheimer's disease and related disorders. Patients with amnestic mild cognitive impairment, the prodrome or transitional stage to Alzheimer's, already show emerging deficits in higher order financial skills, such as conceptual knowledge, bank statement management and bill payment, and also in overall financial capacity (Griffith et al., 2003). Patients with mild Alzheimer's disease have emerging global impairment across almost all financial tasks and most domains, while patients with moderate Alzheimer's disease have advanced global impairment in all financial areas (Marson et al., 2000). While financial capacity is already impaired in patients with mild Alzheimer's disease, a recent longitudinal study has also shown that there is rapid decline, in both simple and complex financial tasks, in mild Alzheimer's disease patients over a one-year period (Martin et al., 2008).

Cognitive Underpinnings

Due to the functional complexity of the financial capacity construct, it is not surprising that there are a wide variety of cognitive abilities that inform financial capacity. Preliminary conceptual work has suggested that financial capacity is comprised of three types of knowledge: declarative knowledge, procedural knowledge, and judgmental abilities. A preliminary neuropsychological study in older adults has suggested that global financial capacity is associated primarily with written arithmetic abilities, and to a lesser extent with memory and executive function skills, in individuals across the demential spectrum: cognitively normal older adults, patients with amnestic mild cognitive impairment, and patients with mild Alzheimer's disease. Much work remains to be done in explicating the cognitive basis of financial capacity across neurocognitive disorders.

Psychiatric and Emotional Factors

Psychiatric and emotional factors can often play a significant role in the assessment of a patient's financial capacity. In some instances, clinical depression or psychotic thinking may affect an individual's ability to carry out basic financial tasks. More commonly, however, such psychiatric conditions will adversely affect an individual's judgment in managing their financial affairs. A protypical example would be the dually diagnosed patient with schizophrenia and a substance abuse disorder, who dissipates his monthly entitlement check on illicit drugs rather than paying for rent, utilities, and his psychotropic medications.

Values

In assessing financial capacity, it is important to obtain information regarding an individual's lifelong values and approach to managing money and finances. As possible examples, has an individual during her adult life been scrupulous and detail oriented regarding her finances, or has she adopted a laissez faire approach and a dependence on others that has sometimes led to financial difficulties? Such information can help the psychologist determine whether an individual's recent problems managing money represent a departure from her premorbid baseline, or are simply an extension of a prior "lifestyle" regarding the management of money. This information in turn can inform the interpretation of evidence and the outcome of the capacity assessment.

It should be noted that a finding of intact financial capacity is not necessarily inconsistent with occasional bad or questionable financial decision making, particularly if eccentric decision making is a lifelong pattern.

Risk Considerations

The capacity to manage one's own finances is a core aspect of personal autonomy in our society, on a par with autonomy to drive a motor vehicle. Accordingly, the tension between autonomy and protection is high with respect to financial capacity: autonomy is highly desirable, but the potential negative consequences for individuals and families of failing capacity are equally strong. Risks of failing financial capacity include poor financial decisions, unintentional self-impoverishment, victimization and exploitation by others, and vulnerability to undue influence.

In assessing financial capacity, an assessment of the relative risks involved in a situation is important. The divorced investment banker with mild dementia who possesses a large stock portfolio and multiple assets presents a different risk profile than the married man with mild dementia living on a fixed income and who has a caring and involved family. Although financial capacity may be impaired in both situations, the outcome of the assessment and the specific intervention(s) recommended can differ substantially based on the risks presented.

Steps to Enhance Capacity

Because financial capacity is such a broad construct, a cognitively or otherwise impaired individual may have preserved financial skills as well as areas of impairment. Supervision regarding financial matters in the home setting may extend and support functioning for a period of time in areas, such as bill payment or checkbook management. However, caution must be exercised with respect to supporting autonomy, insofar as a cognitively impaired individual, despite periodic support, can continue to be highly vulnerable to undue influence and financial predation.

Clinical Judgments of Financial Capacity

Unlike treatment consent capacity, there are currently no published studies of clinician judgments of financial capacity. In large part this paucity reflects the absence of well-accepted conceptual models and instruments for assessing this capacity, and associated empirical research. At the present time, judgments of financial capacity are based on subjective clinical judgment using interview information, capacity remote neuropsychological tests, and in some cases limited props examining basic monetary and other skills or an objective functional assessment instrument.

Judgments of overall financial capacity can be framed using the categorical outcomes of *capable*, *marginally capable*, and *incapable*. Findings regarding specific financial domains and tasks can be referenced as evidence for the overall finding. The distinction between performance and judgment can be incorporated into the clinician's decision-making.

The potential outcome of *marginally capable* (to manage financial affairs) is important and implies limited capacity. It suggests that an individual may retain financial skills in some areas but not others. For example, an elderly person with mild cognitive impairment or early dementia may still be able to perform some financial activities (e.g., handle basic cash transactions, write small checks) but not others (e.g., make investment decisions or asset transfers). This clinical outcome may have particular evidentiary relevance to state conservatorship (guardianship of the estate) proceedings, where courts in a majority of jurisdictions have a legal judgment of limited financial competency available to them.

Clinical Approaches to Assessing Financial Capacity

As is true with other capacities, financial capacity should be evaluated within the context of a general evaluation of an individuals' cognitive and emotional functioning. At present there are two potential approaches to assessing financial capacity: clinical interview and direct performance instruments.

Clinical Interview

The clinical interview is the traditional and currently by far the most widely used method for evaluating financial capacity. At the outset of an interview with patients (and family members), it is important that a clinician first determine the patient's prior or premorbid financial experience and abilities. For example, it would be inappropriate to assume that a person who on testing demonstrates difficulty writing a check has suffered decline in this area, if she has never performed this task, and/or has traditionally delegated this task to a spouse. Once premorbid experience level is established, clinicians need to identify the financial tasks and domains that comprise the patient's current financial activities, and differentially consider those required for independent living within the community. The level of impairment on a specific task or domain should be carefully considered. Individuals who require only verbal prompting to initiate or complete a financial task (e.g., paying bills) are qualitatively different from individuals who require actual hands-on assistance and supervision in paying bills; both, in turn, differ from individuals who are now completely dependent on others to pay their bills.

Some questions to add to a clinical interview that specifically focus on issues relevant to financial capacity are:

1. What is your financial history? Are you in any debt? Do you live week to week? Are you able to plan ahead and save for the future?
2. Do you have enough money to provide for yourself in your retirement?
3. Have you made a will?
4. How knowledgeable are you about financial investments? What, if any, types of investments do you currently have?
5. What are the things you like to spend money on? In spending money, what are your highest priorities?
6. Are there people or organizations to who you generally make gifts or contributions?
7. How would you like to invest and manage your money in the future? Do you want to stick with what you know, or are you open to new investment options?
8. Do you prefer higher-risk investments with a possibility of higher return, or lower-risk investments with a smaller, guaranteed return?
9. If you needed help with your finances, who would you like to help you? Who can you trust to ensure your best interests?
10. How well does this person handle his or her own finances? Is he/she in debt? Does he/she have a good credit record? Is he/she knowledgeable about financial investments?
11. Do you currently have or would you like to obtain a financial advisor? Would this person be a more objective spokesperson than a relative or close friend?
12. Are there certain people with whom you would like your spokesperson to discuss financial decisions on your behalf (family, financial advisors, other)?
13. Is there anyone you specifically would not want to be involved in helping to make financial decisions on your behalf?
14. How closely would you want your spokesperson to follow your instructions about financial decisions, versus what he or she thinks is best for you at the time decisions are made?
15. Are there other things you would like your spokesperson to know about you, if he or she were ever in a position to make financial decisions on your behalf?

Functional Assessment Instruments

Performance-based instruments represent a second approach to assessing financial capacity. In contrast to clinical interview formats, performance-based instruments are not subject to reporter bias. Instead, individuals are asked to perform a series of pragmatic tasks equivalent to those performed in the home and community environment. Performance-based measures are standardized, quantifiable, repeatable, and norm referenced, and thus results can be generalized across patients and settings. These measures can provide clinicians and the courts with objective information regarding performance of specific financial tasks that is relevant to formulation of recommendations and treatment strategies.

Weaknesses of performance-based measures of financial capacity should also be noted. Performance-based measures conducted in a laboratory or clinical office setting cannot take into account either the contextual cues or distractions within the home environment that may assist or interfere with a person's abilities to perform everyday financial tasks. These instruments are more difficult and time-consuming to administer. Given the multi-dimensional and pragmatic aspects of financial capacity, the instruments will also require specialized equipment and training which can make them costly relative to clinical interview.

In comparison to the area of consent capacity, financial capacity has seen only limited instrument development to date. Measures of limited financial skills can be found in a number of broad-based IADL instruments, but there are currently relatively few instruments dedicated to the construct of financial capacity. Different instruments are described in Appendix B.

Case Example

I. Background Information

Mr. Fields, a 75-year-old widowed Caucasian male and construction business owner with a 6th grade education, was referred as an outpatient to the neuropsychology clinic by his daughter, Ms. Daughter, and her attorney, Mr. Legal, Esq., for evaluation of the patient's cognitive and emotional status, and capacities to manage his business and financial affairs and to make a will.

Mr. Fields reportedly has a three- to five-year history of memory problems, which reportedly developed insidiously and have gotten progressively worse. He reportedly has not been previously evaluated for these problems.

In interview, Mr. Fields stated that he does not have any problems with his memory. He also generally denied any other cognitive or functional problems. He stated that he does not have any help at home, but that his daughter comes by sometimes to help him pay bills or to bring him groceries. He denied problems with

---

Instruments to Assess Financial Capacity

Direct Assessment of Functional Status: One subscale

Decision-making Interview for Guardianship: Four vignettes assessing social judgment in financial situations

Financial Capacity Instrument: Comprehensive assessment of nine financial domains and overall financial capacity

Hopemont Capacity Assessment Interview: Three vignettes assessing social judgment in financial situations

Independent Living Scales: One subscale

---

his driving. Regarding mood or personality changes, he reported that he is "doing fine" and denied any symptoms of depression or anxiety.

Mr. Fields's daughter, Ms. Daughter, described a much more serious situation. Ms. Daughter said that her father has had memory problems for at least five years, and that his memory has become noticeably worse over the past three years. She said that she first noticed something was different when she left her accounting job in the family business in 1998 over some disagreements with her uncle James, who co-owns the business with her father. She said that her father did not seem to be taking up for her, which was uncharacteristic of him. She said that she later realized that her father was forgetting about these disagreements and his role in resolving them. Ms. Daughter reported that he currently asks the same question repeatedly, forgets conversations, and constantly misplaces items. She said that he has more trouble remembering people's names. She said that he has comprehension problems, but pretends to understand people when they talk to him. She reported that when they go to restaurants, he gets lost on his way back from the restroom. She reported that he has not driven since July 2000 when he had lung surgery. She said that just prior to that, he complained to her about getting lost while driving in a familiar area.

Regarding functional changes, Ms. Daughter reported that her father has no meaningful activities around the home. He has had full-time caregivers since July 2000. She noted that he still cannot remember their names. She reported that prior to these home health care arrangements, her father was not bathing and was wearing the same clothes every day. She reported that she has handled all of her father's bill paying since October 2000. She said that she also tries to supervise his business transactions. Ms. Daughter reported that her father co-owns an excavation business, Happy Valley Construction, with his brother James. The business is located in Columbus, Georgia. Mr. Fields reportedly has a separate business where he also buys, develops, and sells real estate. She stated that her father has agreed on several occasions to consult her before signing any business documents, but then forgets to do this.

Ms. Daughter reported several poor business decisions her father has made recently. She said that in the past year he sold a piece of real estate for $10,000 that was worth $250,000. She also reported that he has made almost $500,000 in loans to the family business over the past two years, and that these loans have not been repaid. She reported that her father initially loaned $200,000 to Happy Valley in 1998, $90,000 of which went to his nephew, who also works for the company. She stated that there does not appear to be a note for the loan to his nephew. She reported that the remaining $300,000 was loaned out in October 2000. Ms. Daughter said that she has also recently discovered a buy/sell agreement, signed by her father while she was out of town, which states that if her father dies, the company will go to her uncle James and the money owed by the company to her father will be forgiven. She noted that in this buy/sell agreement, some property that belongs to her father is listed instead as company property.

Regarding mood or personality changes, Ms. Daughter reported that her father is more laid back and even indifferent. She said that he used to be very focused on and concerned about his business affairs, but now does not seem concerned about them. She denied symptoms of anxiety or depression, but noted that he naps a lot during the day. She also stated that he always wants to eat because he forgets that he has already eaten.

Social/Academic/Occupational History: Mr. Fields reportedly was born and raised in Columbus, Georgia. He reported that he had four brothers and sisters. The patient's father was a farmer and iron smith. The patient was reportedly married for 40 years when his wife died in 1990. He reported that he has two daughters and one son with a disability. He currently lives alone.

Mr. Fields reportedly completed six years of education. He reportedly buys and sells real estate and co-owns an excavation business called Happy Valley Construction Company.

Prior Medical History: Mr. Fields's medical history reportedly is significant for diabetes and history of blood clots. Surgical history reportedly includes four-way coronary artery bypass graft (1989) and partial lung resection (2000). The patient reportedly does not drink alcohol and does not smoke. There is reportedly no history of alcohol or other substance abuse.

Family medical history is reportedly positive for myocardial infarction in his brother, stomach cancer in his sister, skin cancer in his sister, and possible Alzheimer's disease in his mother.

Psychiatric History: Mr. Fields reportedly has no history of mental health treatment. As noted above, he reportedly has had no prior evaluations for his memory problems.

Medications: Coumadin, Exelon, Tenormin, ginkgo biloba, Ambien, Detrol, Claritin.

II. Behavioral Observations

Mr. Fields presented as a well-groomed, nicely dressed 75-year-old Caucasian man. He was accompanied to the evaluation by his daughter.

In interview, the patient's speech was fluent and reasonably goal-directed but lacked spontaneity. Responses were impoverished. Comprehension appeared generally intact. Affect was mildly constricted, and mood was pleasant but irritable. Insight was judged to be very poor. There was no indication or report of formal hallucinations or delusions, or of a thought or perceptual disorder. There was no indication of suicidal ideation, plan, or intent.

During testing, Mr. Fields was alert and pleasant but would quickly become irritable and uncooperative with testing. He exhibited mild performance anxiety. He displayed task frustration by abandoning or avoiding tasks. He showed no response to encouragement from the psychometric technician. He displayed inability to complete some tasks due to comprehension problems. He made a few perseverative and intrusion errors. He required constant redirection to task. He showed a complete lack of test-taking strategies.

Mr. Fields was irritable and at times uncooperative during the testing. At one point, he refused to continue testing and started to leave, but was persuaded by his daughter to continue. Because of his reluctance to participate, and the examiner's concern that he would prematurely terminate the testing, only an abbreviated test battery could be administered. Nevertheless, sufficient information was obtained to respond fully to the referral questions. Overall, the patient appeared to put forth variable but acceptable effort during the testing. Much of his reluctance to participate related to tasks that he appeared unable to perform. Overall, the current test results are an accurate representation of Mr. Fields's current levels of cognitive and emotional functioning, and of his current financial abilities.

III. Tests Administered

California Verbal Learning Test - II (CVLT-II)
Clinical Interview
Cognitive Competency
Executive Clock Drawing Task (CLOX)
Financial Capacity Instrument
Geriatric Depression Scale (GDS)
Mattis Dementia Rating Scale (DRS)
Token Test
Trails A and B
WAB Auditory Comprehension
Wide Range Achievement Test-3(reading subtest)

IV. Impressions and Summary
Neuropsychological Findings
1. *Probable dementia, currently moderate (DRS=89/144, CDR= 2.0).*

The neuropsychological test results were consistent with probable moderate dementia.

Evidence for this impression included severe impairment on a dementia screening instrument and impairments in high-load verbal learning, recall, and recognition memory (severe to profound), simple short-term verbal recall (severe), orientation to time (severe), orientation to place (severe), simple auditory comprehension (severe), reading abilities (moderate), visuospatial construction of a clock drawing (mild), simple visuomotor tracking (mild), propositional auditory comprehension (moderate), and spontaneous construction of a clock drawing (severe). The patient was unable to complete a measure of visuomotor tracking/set flexibility. In addition, the patient's daughter reported that he has had progressive memory and other cognitive problems for as long as five years.

Functional testing and interview data were also consistent with moderate dementia. Mr. Fields was severely impaired on a cognitive measure of everyday problem solving abilities. On a functional measure of financial capacity, the patient showed intact performance only on simple tasks of naming coins/currency, coin/currency relationships, and single and multi-item grocery purchases. He demonstrated significant impairment on tests of counting coins/currency, understanding financial concepts, making change for a vending machine, tipping, conceptual understanding of a checkbook/register, pragmatic use of a checkbook/register, conceptual understanding of a bank statement, use of a bank statement, detection of telephone fraud, conceptual understanding of bills, identifying and prioritizing bills, and knowledge of his personal financial assets and activities. In addition, the patient's daughter indicated that he has home health care aides around the clock. She reported that prior to these arrangements, the patient was not bathing and wore the same clothes every day. She said that he currently has no meaningful activities around the home.

2. *Possible Alzheimer s disease.*

Mr. Fields's neurocognitive profile was consistent with possible Alzheimer's disease. High-load verbal learning, recall, and recognition memory were moderately to severely impaired and he was unable to benefit from semantic or recognition cueing. He showed 0% recall after a short delay, which is consistent with the rapid decay of information over delay seen in Alzheimer's disease. In addition, he had 0% short-term recall of verbal items from the memory subtest of the DRS. Characteristic impairments on measures of executive function (simple visuomotor tracking, propositional auditory comprehension, and spontaneous construction of a clock drawing) and inability to complete a measure of visuomotor tracking/set flexibility. Due to the patient's reluctance to cooperate, a more comprehensive evaluation of memory, attention, expressive language, and verbal intellectual abilities was not possible.

Clinical course was consistent with Alzheimer's disease. Mr. Fields's cognitive difficulties reportedly have slowly progressed over the past five years. He also has a family history of possible Alzheimer's disease.

In the examiner's judgment, it is highly probable that Mr. Fields has Alzheimer's disease. However, he needs a neurological work-up for dementia before the clinical diagnosis can established conclusively.

Capacity Findings

1. Probable current incapacity to manage business-related and everyday financial affairs.

History, interview, and test data indicated that Mr. Fields is currently incapable of managing his financial affairs and making business-related decisions. In interview, Mr. Fields demonstrated inaccurate knowledge of his financial and business affairs. For example, the patient indicated that he goes into work at his excavation business every day, even occasionally running construction equipment, whereas the patient's daughter reported that he is retired and that his brother operates and manages the business on his own. She reported that her father continues to manage his own finances, but makes poor business decisions (e.g., recently sold some property for 10% of what it was worth). She reported that her father has agreed several times not to sign anything without letting her review it first, but then forgets to consult her. She said that he has also made several large loans to his business recently, but seems generally unaware of these loans and the fact that they are not being repaid.

Functional testing of financial abilities revealed overall severe impairment in financial capacity. On testing, Mr. Fields demonstrated intact performance on tasks of naming coins/currency, coin/currency relationships, and single and multi-item cash purchases. However, he was impaired on tests of counting coins/currency, understanding financial concepts, making change for a vending machine, tipping, conceptual understanding of a checkbook, use of a checkbook, conceptual understanding of a bank statement, use of a bank statement, detection of telephone fraud, conceptual understanding of bills, identifying and prioritizing bills, and knowledge of personal financial activities.

Taken together, these findings indicate that Mr. Fields is no longer capable of managing any aspect of his business and financial affairs.

2. Probable vulnerability to undue influence.

Early on in their disease course, patients with Alzheimer's disease and related dementias become increasingly vulnerable to the influence of others. It is possible that Mr. Fields's reported recent poor business decisions may reflect such a vulnerability. For example, during testing Mr. Fields failed to detect a telephone credit card scam situation and agreed to provide his credit card number over the phone to an unknown caller.

V. Recommendations

1. We recommend that Mr. Fields be referred for a neurological and dementia evaluation.
2. Continued pharmacotherapy with cholinesterase inhibitors is appropriate.
3. Mr. Fields and his family should consider legally securing his business, financial, and personal affairs as soon as possible. Mr. Fields could potentially benefit from formal conservatorship. Given his level of dementia and functional impairments, formal guardianship should also be considered.
4. Mr. Fields's cognitive and emotional status should continue to be closely monitored.

Testamentary Capacity

Introduction

Under Anglo-American law, the right of testation refers to the freedom to choose how one's property and other possessions will be disposed of following death. In order for a will to be valid, the testator (person making the will) must have testamentary capacity at the time that the will is executed. Testamentary capacity is, thus, a legal construct that represents that level of mental capacity necessary to execute a valid will. If testamentary capacity is absent, then the will is void and fails. For reasons of public policy supporting the orderly probating of wills and distribution of assets to heirs, courts have traditionally applied a low legal threshold for finding testamentary capacity (Marson & Hebert, 2008b).

Conceptually testamentary capacity falls within the broader concept of *financial capacity*, but for reasons of history and tradition testamentary capacity continues to receive distinct attention within the legal system. Each state jurisdiction, through its statutes and case law, sets forth legal elements or criteria for testamentary capacity. Although requirements for testamentary capacity vary across states, four criteria have generally been identified. A testator must know what a will is; have knowledge of his/her potential heirs; have knowledge of the nature and extent of his/her assets; and have a general plan of distribution of assets to heirs. The absence of one or more of these elements of testamentary capacity can serve as grounds for a court to invalidate a will. As discussed further below, a will can also fail if the testator has an *insane delusion* that specifically and materially affects the testator's creation or amendment of a will. Finally, a will is often challenged on the conceptually separate ground that it was the product of *undue influence* on the testator exerted by a family member or third party (see separate chapter on undue influence in this book). (Marson et al., 2008b).

As testamentary capacity represents a legal construct closely associated with the testator's mental status, clinicians are often asked to evaluate testamentary capacity and offer clinical testimony in legal proceedings. Such evaluations are sometimes conducted contemporaneously with a will's execution, but more often occur retrospectively following the incapacity or death of a testator and probating of the will. In recent years there has been an increase in will contests in the probate courts, with associated claims of impaired testamentary capacity and also undue influence (Marson et al., 2008b).

Legal Elements/Standards

Although requirements for testamentary capacity vary across states, four criteria have generally been identified. A testator must have (1) knowledge of what a will is; (2) knowledge of that class of individuals that represents the testator's potential heirs ("natural objects of one's bounty"); (3) knowledge of the nature and extent of one's assets; and (4) a general plan of distribution of assets to heirs.

The absence of one or more of these elements can serve as grounds for a court to invalidate a will due to lack of testamentary capacity. However, the way in which courts weigh legal elements of testamentary capacity in determining the validity of a will varies across states. Some states require that the testator meet only one of the criteria for a will to be valid. Other states require that the testator not only understand a will and demonstrate memory of all property and potential heirs, but also hold this information in mind while developing a plan for disposition of assets. Accordingly, the reader is strongly encouraged to review the relevant law on testamentary capacity specific to his/her state jurisdiction (Marson et al., 2008b).

As discussed in the section below, the functional elements of testamentary capacity are almost entirely cognitive. To exercise testamentory capacity, however, one must communicate and work with an attorney, which introduces a professional relationship and some element of social discourse into the exercise of this capacity.

Functional Elements

In the case of testamentary capacity, the functional elements are best understood as reflections of the underlying legal elements. Testamentary capacity is analogous to consent capacity insofar as it is a highly verbal mediated capacity with no pragmatic skills or demands other than a signature on the legal document. Thus the functional elements inherent to testamentary capacity would include the cognitive abilities to generally describe what a will is, to recall and name potential heirs (objects of bounty), to describe generally the nature and extent of assets includable within a person's will, and to outline very generally a potential plan of distribution of assets to heirs.

Cognitive Underpinnings

Given the "purely" cognitive basis of the testamentary capacity construct, it will be important over time to identify discrete cognitive functions that inform each of the legal (and functional) elements. Marson and colleagues have done some initial conceptual work in this area (Marson, Huthwaite, & Hebert, 2004), but true delineation of these cognitive sources awaits empirical confirmation.

1. Cognitive Functions Related to Understanding the Nature of a Will

This element requires a testator to understand the purposes and consequences of a will, and to express these verbally or in some other adequate form to an attorney or judge. Possible cognitive functions involved may include semantic memory regarding terms such as death, property and inheritance, verbal abstraction and comprehension abilities, and sufficient language abilities to express the testator's understanding. A testator's signature on a legal document by itself does not demonstrate understanding, as a signature is an automatic procedural behavior not dependent upon higher level cognition (Greiffenstein, 1996).

2. Cognitive Functions Related to Knowing the Nature and Extent of Property

The second legal element of testamentary capacity requires that the testator remember the nature and extent of his or her property to be disposed. As reported earlier, some states differ in their interpretation of this (Walsh et al., 1997). Possible cognitive functions involved here would include semantic memory concerning assets and ownership, historical memory and short-term memory enabling recall of long-term and more recently acquired assets and property, and comprehension of the value attached to different assets and property. If the testator has recently purchased new possessions prior to his or her execution of a will, then impairment in short-term memory (the hallmark sign of early Alzheimer's disease) can significantly impact his or her recall of these items. Testators also must be able to form working estimates of value for key pieces of property that reasonably approximate their true value; it is likely that executive function abilities play a role here (Marson et al., 2004).

3. Cognitive Functions Related to Knowing the Objects of One's Bounty

This legal element requires that the testator be cognizant of those individuals who represent his natural heirs, or other heirs who can place a reasonable claim on the estate. Autobiographical memory would appear to be a prominent cognitive ability associated with this element. As dementias like Alzheimer's disease progress, testators may be increasingly unable to recall family members and acquaintances, leading ultimately to failures to recognize these individuals in photographs or even when presented in person (Marson et al., 2004).

4. Cognitive Functions Related to a Plan for Distribution of Assets

This final legal element of testamentary capacity requires that the testator be able to express a basic plan for distributing his assets to his intended heirs. Insofar as this element integrates the first three elements in a supraordinate fashion, the proposed cognitive basis for this element arguably represents an integration of the cognitive abilities underlying the other three elements. Accordingly, executive function abilities are implied as the testator must demonstrate a projective understanding of how future dispositions of specific property to specific heirs will occur (Marson et al., 2004).

Psychiatric and Emotional Factors Related to Testamentary Capacity

Severe psychiatric disorders like schizophrenia and bipolar disorder can affect testamentary capacity in different respects. In some cases, the level of emotional disturbance may be sufficient to affect the individual's cognitive understanding of one or more of the legal elements. However, even if an individual with psychiatric illness can meet the legal elements for testamentary capacity, the will can still fail if the psychiatric illness is specific to the testamentary disposition. Thus, if a testator refuses to include a child in a will due to a psychiatric delusion that the child is stealing from her or trying to injure her, that could be properly challenged under the *insane delusion* doctrine outlined above. The notion here is that but for the specific delusion, the testator would be including the child in a will that would meet the requirements for probate (Marson et al., 2008b).

Diagnostic Considerations

As a cognitively mediated capacity, testamentary capacity is sensitive to a variety of medical conditions that affect cognitive and behavioral functioning. Medical conditions that impair testamentary capacity include neurodegenerative disorders like Alzheimer's disease and Parkinson's disease, acquired neurological injuries like traumatic brain injury, and developmental disorders, such as mental retardation and autism. In addition, as discussed above, severe psychiatric disorders like schizophrenia and bipolar disorder can affect testamentary capacity in different respects.

There is very little empirical research to date in the area of testamentary capacity, and none specific to the effects of different diagnostic conditions on testamentary capacity. This remains an area where considerable valuable research can be done.

Values

The capacity to distribute assets and other personal possessions following death is an important right and valued aspect of personal autonomy in our society. For reasons of public policy, courts invoke a low legal threshold for upholding wills and permitting legal transfer of property after death. Thus, the values and interests of the testator are given considerable weight by courts. In assessing testamentary capacity, as in financial capacity, it is important to obtain information regarding an individual's lifelong values about money, personal property, and finances. In this regard, important information can be ascertained by reviewing prior wills of a testator, which will reflect the application of his/her values to the assignment of property to designated heirs. A testator's radical departure from prior testamentary value patterns in a new will, known legally as an "unnatural will," may lead a court to consider whether a testator is suffering from diminished capacity or from coercion through the effects of undue influence. As an example, one of the authors was involved in a case where the testator, a woman, had predicated prior wills firmly on the principle of keeping the federal tax consequences of any will as limited as possible. In later life, after developing a dementia and falling under the influence of an unscrupulous family friend and neighbor, her wills demonstrated a total disregard for tax consequences, but a remarkable attention to the financial needs and benefits of the neighbor. This will was challenged on grounds both of impaired testamentary capacity and undue influence, and the change in the testator's value assumptions underlying the new will became a key argument for the party challenging the validity of that will.

Risk Assessment

The financial stakes are very high with respect to will transfers of assets, which can involve substantial monetary amounts. The number of will contests has increased significantly in the past 20 years, due to factors such as the increase in blended families and associated conflicts in family agendas, and the enormous transfer of wealth currently occurring between the World War II generation and the Baby Boomer generation (estimated at anywhere between $6 trillion and $16 trillion). The low legal threshold applied for upholding testamentary capacity has as its inevitable counterpart the increased risk that a cognitively impaired testator will make an inappropriate or unintended disposition, or be subjected to undue influence in which testamentary intent is supplanted by the will of the influencer. As a practical matter, it is crucial that family members take steps to ensure that a cognitively impaired older adult family member (prototypically, the widow who insists on living alone and resists any outside help) is supported and protected in her financial and testamentary activities. This can be a delicate matter for families, but, in general, a level of concern is justified given the rampant financial exploitation of older adults that is occurring nationwide.

Steps to Enhance Capacity

Due to its cognitive basis and relatively modest cognitive demands, testamentary capacity is a capacity that can be readily supported or enhanced. All of the elements of testamentary capacity can be discussed ahead of time with the testator, and relevant material such as potential heirs or assets/possessions can be rehearsed prior to will execution. As part of such support efforts, it is important to ensure throughout the process that the testator is acting in a voluntary way and is not subject to direct or indirect coercion or influence.

An assessment of the patient's awareness of cognitive deficits can be an important part of the task of enhancing capacity. There is an ethical imperative to preserve and support autonomous decisions of the patient wherever possible. An individual's awareness is often critical to how well he or she might be able to compensate for cognitive deficits. That is, those individuals with a significant lack of awareness will not see any need to try and compensate for deficits, whereas those individuals with awareness will be open to compensatory strategies. Thus the clinician

should investigate the patient's awareness of deficits and openness to potential compensatory strategies. In their 1997 practice guideline on capacity assessment for psychologists in the Veterans Affairs system, the authors noted the importance of assessing awareness of deficits (U.S. Department of Veterans Affairs, 1997).

Clinical Judgments of Testamentary Capacity

Similar to financial capacity, there are currently no published studies of clinician judgments of financial capacity known to the authors. There are also no empirically validated assessment instruments currently available. A testamentary capacity information collection form was developed by attorney Baird Brown and co-authors (Walsh et al. 1994). At the present time, judgments of testamentary capacity are based on subjective clinical judgment and experience using patient and collateral interview information, inventories of patient assets and potential heirs, and more or less structured evaluations of cognitive and psychiatric functioning. Valuable recommendations for conducting clinical assessments of testamentary capacity has been offered by forensic psychiatrists (Spar & Garb, 1992; Shulman et al., 2007).

Judgments of testamentary capacity can be framed using the categorical outcomes of *capable* and *incapable,* and in certain instances *marginally capable.* The evidence regarding each legal (functional) element should be detailed, including comparisons of the testator's belief and knowledge with actual externally confirmed accounts of heirs and asset possession. The potential outcome of *marginally capable* may be important in some cases of prospective assessment where the testator's capacity is borderline as a result of cognitive, psychiatric, or other medical conditions, but nonetheless may be supportable in various ways.

Clinical Approaches to Assessing Testamentary Capacity

Clinical consultation regarding testamentary capacity can substantially inform the way in which attorneys and judges understand and determine legal issues of testamentary capacity. The roles of clinicians in cases of testamentary capacity include informal consulting with attorneys about adults with questionable capacity, contemporaneous clinical evaluations of testamentary capacity prior to will execution, and retrospective evaluations of testamentary capacity in cases involving a now deceased or incapable testator, discussed in turn below

Functional Assessment Instruments

There are no empirically validated standardized instruments to assess testamentary capacity.

Consultation Regarding Testamentary Capacity

An attorney may choose to consult with a clinician prior to, or instead of, seeking a formal clinical assessment. In this situation, the clinician provides an informal opinion regarding testamentary capacity based solely on adult observations and information provided by the attorney. The clinician may also identify concerns or issues that the attorney may have overlooked, as well as suggest strategies for enhancing testamentary capacity. Clinical consultation may assuage an attorney's concern regarding an adult's testamentary capacity, or justify pursuing a formal clinical evaluation of testamentary capacity.

Contemporaneous Clinical Evaluation of Testamentary Capacity

In certain circumstances the testator, or his/her attorney or family member, may request that a clinician assess the testator's testamentary capacity prior to will execution. Two scenarios are common to such a referral. The attorney may have concerns about testamentary capacity and desire clinical expertise and input on the issue before proceeding further. Alternatively, in cases of ongoing or anticipated family conflict, the attorney may seek to preempt a future will contest by having an assessment of testamentary capacity conducted as part of the will execution.

Contemporaneous evaluations of testamentary capacity are multi-faceted and involve (1) collecting relevant data regarding the testator's assets, potential heirs, and general cognitive and everyday functioning from collateral sources (i.e., a spouse, other family members, and friends), (2) conducting a comprehensive mental status examination of the testator to identify cognitive and psychiatric impairments that may interfere with testamentary capacity, and (3) completing a thorough clinical interview of the testator that assesses testamentary capacity according to the above legal criteria. Spar and Garb have proposed a valuable semi-structured interview approach that clinicians can use to structure an interview regarding testamentary capacity (Spar et al., 1992) (see also Shulman et al., 2007). Because the validity of a will is dependent upon the testator's capacity at the specific time that the will is executed, clinicians should conduct evaluations of testamentary capacity as close to the time of will execution as possible (Marson et al., 2008b).

Retrospective Evaluation of Testamentary Capacity

Although contemporaneous assessment of testamentary capacity is highly desirable, retrospective evaluations probably represent the majority of these forensic assessments. Retrospective evaluations arise after the death or incompetency of a testator, when potential heirs or other parties contest a will on grounds that the testator lacked testamentary capacity at the time that the will was executed. Retrospective evaluations of testamentary capacity are based upon a thorough record review and information obtained from the testator's family, friends, business associates, and other involved professionals (often through deposition testimony). Primary attention is given to gathering evidence of mental status, neurobehavioral, and everyday functional skills occurring as close as possible to the date that the will was executed. Relevant personal records include the testator's business records, checkbook and other financial documents, and personal documents (e.g., letters, diaries, family films or videos, etc.). Medical records can yield particularly useful information, including mental status, behavioral observations, diagnosis, level of impairment, dementia stage (if applicable), and psychological test results. Clinicians may also find it beneficial to interview the testator's surviving family, friends, business associates, and other involved professionals regarding the testator's cognitive and functional abilities at the time that the will was executed.

Ultimately, the clinician must assemble all of this information and retrospectively determine whether or not the testator clinically had testamentary capacity at the prior relevant legal time point(s). In some cases it may not be possible to render such a judgment, if there is insufficient evidence of the testator's cognitive, emotional, and functional abilities contemporaneous with the prior will execution.

With respect to both contemporaneous and retrospective forensic evaluations of testamentary capacity, it is important to emphasize that the clinician's opinions regarding testamentary capacity represent clinical judgments that the court may consider and weigh in arriving at a dispositive legal judgment of testamentary capacity (Marson et al., 2008b).

Recommended Steps in Conducting a Retrospective Evaluation of Testamentary Capacity

1   Identify the operative legal standard for testamentary capacity in your state jurisdiction. For example, in Michigan there are three criteria (*Persinger v. Holst*, 2001 Michigan Court of Appeals):
    a. to comprehend the nature and extent of his or her property,
    b. to recall the objects of his or her bounty, and
    c. to determine and understand the distribution of his or her property.
2. Organize medical, legal, and other records relevant to the capacity issue. Creating a chronological timeline reflecting important medical and lay contacts, and relevant legal transactions, is essential to organizing the information an expert is asked to review.
3. Where possible, contact and speak with individuals who knew the decedent testator and can offer informed lay judgments about mental status at the time of will execution.

4. Obtain information about the attorneys involved in the will execution. Who was the attorney and what history did he or she have with the adult? Was there a single discussion about the will between the adult and attorney or multiple discussions? Did the attorney make notes at the time the will was created or changed?
5. Assess for the presence and severity of a mental disorder at the time of will execution. With older adults, the most often disputed wills are those that were made or modified when an individual had a memory disorder or a diagnosed dementia. Is there evidence, through medical records, of a mental disorder that might affect cognitive and emotional abilities related to the elements of testamentary capacity? In some cases, there may be specific neuropsychological test information that will shed light on mental capacity relevant to testamentary capacity.
6. In cases of dementia, seek to determine the stage of dementia as it can significantly inform the clinical judgment of testamentary capacity. The Clinical Dementia Rating (CDR) (Morris, 1993) represents one such dementia staging tool. Because the legal threshold for testamentary capacity is low, an individual with mild dementia may still be capable of making a new will, whereas a patient with more advanced dementia may no longer recognize the objects of his bounty, or know the nature and extent of his property. However, as discussed throughout this handbook, every capacity matter is individual-specific and, irrespective of dementia stage, requires an analysis of the individual's mental status and condition in relation to the particular jurisdictional elements for testamentary capacity.
7. Assess testamentary capacity by determining whether there is clinical and other evidence in the record supporting the critical legal elements of this capacity. In some cases there may be insufficient evidence in the record to support a clinical judgment of testamentary capacity.
8. In addition to offering a capacity judgment, a psychologist or other expert is often well-positioned to offer a retrospective opinion

regarding the possible role of undue influence in will procurement. Most will contest cases will involve an associated, alternative legal claim of undue influence, with the contention that even if the testator possessed residual testamentary capacity, it was supplanted by the actions of a third party influencer. Undue influence is discussed in more detail in Chapter 7.

Case Study of Prospective Assessment of Testamentary Capacity

I.   Referral and Background Information

Ms. Milton was referred as an outpatient to the Clinical Neuropsychology Laboratory by Dr. Psychiatrist for evaluation of testamentary capacity.

History of Present Illness: Ms. Milton has been followed by Dr. Psychiatrist for treatment of anxiety and depression. She has decided to make changes in her will and wants to ensure that the new will will not be challenged. Dr. Psychiatrist recommended that she have a formal evaluation to assess testamentary capacity, and referred her to the Clinical Neuropsychology Laboratory.

In interview with the examiners, Ms. Milton denied significant changes in cognitive functioning. She acknowledged occasionally losing her train of thought, but denied memory loss that interferes with her daily life. She also denied difficulties with language, visuospatial, motor, or sensory function.

Ms. Milton denied significant changes in her daily functioning and in her emotional state. She reported that she cooks, does chores, and babysits her granddaughter. She denied depression and stated that she was feeling pretty good. Ms. Milton acknowledged anxiety regarding the sale of the family business.

In the interview, Ms. Milton responded appropriately and knowledgeably to questions regarding testamentary capacity. She defined a will as the "distribution of property of a person who is deceased according to their wishes." She provided a comprehensive description of her property and assets, which appeared informed and accurate. Ms. Milton also provided a complete list of her immediate descendants and potential beneficiaries of her will. She described her planned division of her estate into four equal shares for her husband, son, daughter, and her granddaughter (daughter's child). She indicated that she was not planning to include her grandson (son's child) in the will, but provided a clear and reasonable explanation. She stated that her decision was based upon her relationship with this child.

The patient's daughter, Ms. Daughter, reported a similar situation concerning her mother's health. She denied changes in her mother's memory, language, visuospatial, motor, and sensory function. She reported that her mother shows good judgment in everyday activities. Ms. Daughter stated that her mother picks up her granddaughter from preschool every day and has no problems with babysitting her. Ms. Daughter also indicated that there has been no change in her mother's activities around the house and she continues to cook, perform small chores, read, and manage her checkbook. She reported that her mother does not currently appear to be depressed.

Prior Medical History: The patient's medical and surgical history is reportedly positive for tuberculosis and removal of the upper lobe of her right lung (age 16), hysterectomy (1970), cholecystectomy, breast cancer with right radical mastectomy (12-14 years ago; there has been no recurrence); and hospitalization for acute bronchitis (19xx). Ms. Milton also reported bladder incontinence, kidney problems, diverticulitis, ulcers (which she attributed to stress regarding her children and her business), and multiple hospitalizations for tachycardia. She reported breaking her wrist in the early 19xxs. She indicated that she had an adverse reaction to the anesthesia and "died on the table." Ms. Milton reported respiratory difficulty since that time. She also reported initial memory difficulties that resolved over time. Family history is reportedly positive for cancer (father), ulcers (father), and circulatory problems (mother). The patient's mother reportedly experienced cognitive changes following a limb amputation.

Psychiatric History: Ms. Milton's history is positive for inpatient and outpatient psychiatric treatment. She reported seeking treatment for depression following her hysterectomy and the illness of her parents (approximately 1970). Ms.

Milton indicated additional treatment for depression following her father's death in the mid-1970s. In 19xx she reportedly intentionally overdosed on sleeping pills, came close to dying, and was hospitalized for psychiatric treatment. She reported approximately five inpatient hospitalizations, including treatment for depression and dependence on sleeping pills and pain medication. Ms. Milton reportedly saw Dr. Shrink for many years in the 1980s and early 1990s. She has seen Dr. Psychiatrist for depression associated with her hospitalization in 1996, family difficulties, and dependence on prescription medications.

Medications: Verapamil, Atenolol, Propulsid.

Social/Academic/ Occupational History: Ms. Milton is an only child who inherited the family funeral home. Her husband managed the business after her father died. Her son, Mr. Son, is currently managing the business, although her husband remains active in the business. Ms. Milton's daughter also works in the family business. Ms. Milton has been approached about selling the funeral home and there has been some family disagreement regarding the sale. The patient reported anxiety regarding the sale and distress that her children do not get along well. Ms. Milton also described a close relationship with her granddaughter (Ms. Daughter's daughter) and reported frequent contact with her. She stated that she does not often see her grandson (Mr. Son's son) and indicated some conflict with her daughter-in-law.

Ms. Milton reportedly completed 12 years of education with an overall grade average of "A." She is the owner of her family business.

II. Behavioral Observations

Ms. Milton presented as a nicely dressed and well-groomed 66-year-old Caucasian female. She was accompanied to the evaluation by her daughter.

In the interview, speech was goal oriented and responsive, but mildly slurred with strained and hypernasal vocal quality. These speech difficulties are probably attributable to dentures and Ms. Milton's history of respiratory difficulty. Affect was full. Mood was pleasant, but somewhat serious and anxious. The patient appeared candid and forthright.

In the testing, Ms. Milton was alert and pleasant. Some mild performance anxiety was noted, but the patient responded appropriately to encouragement and handled frustration appropriately. No expressive or receptive language difficulties were noted. There was no loss of task, cognitive rigidity, or spoiling. There were a few perseverations and intrusions.

Ms. Milton appeared to put forth a good effort throughout the testing. The current results appear to be a valid representation of her current level of cognitive and emotional functioning.

III. Tests Administered

Aphasia Series
Apraxia Series
Beck Depression Inventory
Benton Visual Form Discrimination Test (VFDT)
Boston Naming Test (BNT)
California Verbal Learning Test (CVLT)
Cognitive Competency
Construction Series
Dementia Rating Scale (DRS)
Financial Capacity Instrument (FCI)
Neurodiagnostic Interview
Premorbid Verbal IQ Estimate (Barona)
Shanan Sentence Completion Test (SSCT)
Trails
Visual Series
Wechsler Memory Scale-Revised (WMS-R)
Wechsler Adult Intelligence Scale-Revised (WAIS-R)

IV. Summary of Test Results

Orientation: Ms. Milton was fully oriented to person, place, and time.

Attention and Concentration: General attention and concentration was in the low average range for age group (23th %ile). Simple visuomotor tracking was in the low average range for age, sex, and educational level (27th %ile). Auditory attention was in the high average range for digits forward (83th %ile) and in the mildly impaired range for digits backward (9th %ile). Visual attention was in the low average range for forward sequencing (17th %ile) and backward sequencing (21th %ile).

Language: Spontaneous speech was mildly slurred with strained and hypernasal vocal quality.

Confrontation naming was in the average range for age (44th %ile).

Simple auditory comprehension was intact. Reading comprehension was generally intact relative to a neurologically intact geriatric sample.

Memory Function: Short-term verbal memory fell in the high average range for age group (81st percentile). Delayed recall (30-minute) for verbal material was also in the high average range (75th percentile), with 81% retention of learned verbal material.

Short-term visual memory was in the average range for age group (68th percentile). Delayed recall (30-minute) for visual material was in the moderately impaired range for age group (1st percentile), with no retention of learned visual material. Ms. Milton appeared to have difficulty in recognizing which visual patterns she was required to reproduce.

High-load verbal acquisition was in the mildly impaired range (4th percentile). Short-term recall (5 minute span) and delayed recall (20 minute span) were in the low average range. Semantic cueing enhanced recall from mildly impaired to intact performance. There were a few perseverations and intrusions. Recognition memory was intact.

Visuospatial Function: Simple visual field perception was intact. Visual form discrimination was in the mildly impaired range with peripheral and rotation errors.

Visuospatial construction for simple and complex geometric figures was intact. Block construction fell in the average range for age (25%ile).

Fine Motor Functioning: Bimanual motor planning was intact. Simple and complex ideomotor hand functioning was intact bilaterally.

Intelligence and Higher Cognitive Functioning: The patient obtained a WAIS-R Verbal IQ of 105, which placed her current level of verbal intellectual functioning in the average range for age (63rd percentile). This score was comparable to a premorbid estimate of 106 (Barona).

The patient obtained a WAIS-R Performance IQ of 93, which placed her current level of nonverbal intellectual functioning in the average range for age (32nd percentile). This score was somewhat lower than expected from a premorbid estimate of 104 (Barona).

The patient obtained a WAIS-R Full Scale IQ of 100, which placed her current level of intellectual functioning in the average range for age (50th percentile). This score was comparable to a premorbid estimate of 105 (Barona).

Mental Flexibility and Executive Function: On a test of visuomotor tracking and set flexibility, the patient performed in the mildly impaired range (7th percentile). The patient's spontaneous clock drawing indicated possible very mild impairment in executive functioning. Ms. Milton had slight difficulty in placing the clock hands and distributing numbers around the clock face.

Social Comprehension and Judgment: On a cognitive measure of everyday problem solving, Ms. Milton demonstrated mildly impaired functioning, relative to a neurologically intact geriatric sample. Incorrect responses reflected some insensitivity to threats to personal safety.

General conceptual comprehension was in the high average range (85th percentile).

Financial Capacity: On a measurement of financial capacity, Ms. Milton demonstrated mild impairment in small cash transactions, relative to a neurologically intact geriatric sample. Financial judgment was in the low-average range. Basic monetary skills, financial conceptual knowledge, checkbook management, and bank statement management were intact.

Personality Functioning: On a self-report inventory of depressive symptomatology, Ms. Milton endorsed symptoms of self-criticism, concern about physical appearance, decreased motivation, fatigue, and somatic concerns. Overall, her responses did not indicate the presence of significant depression.

On a semi-projective sentence completion test, Ms. Milton demonstrated coping mechanisms that were primarily active (When she saw that others did better than she: "she decided to try harder"; When she was attacked she: "fought back"). Responses reflected a variable self concept (People think I: "am fat"; She often thinks she is: "very happy"). Ms. Milton's responses also indicated aims and frustrations that were primarily externally directed.

V. Impression

1. **Generally intact cognitive and emotional functioning for age, education, and occupational attainment (DRS = 140/144), with isolated cognitive deficits.**

   The neuropsychological test results indicated generally intact cognitive functioning. The patient's performance indicated intact functioning across domains of language, short-term memory, visuospatial construction, fine motor functioning, and intellectual functioning. There were isolated mild deficits in high-load verbal acquisition, visual form discrimination, and mental flexibility, moderate impairment in delayed visual memory, and possible decline in attention/concentration. Ms. Milton also demonstrated some mild deficits in functional abilities indicating some insensitivity to threats to personal safety, and difficulties with small cash transactions and financial judgment.

   The interview and psychological testing also revealed adequate emotional functioning. Ms. Milton denied depression during interview and on a self-report inventory. She acknowledged anxiety surrounding the sale of her business, but this did not appear to be affecting her overall functioning.

2. **Probable intact testamentary capacity.**

   The patient demonstrated sufficient specific knowledge of the testamentary process to indicate current capacity to make a will. She provided an adequate description of the function of a will. She produced a reasonable account of her property and listed those relations whose interests would be affected by her will. She produced coherent and adequate reasons for the inclusion and exclusion of relations in her will.

   The neuropsychological and psychological testing also supported the patient's testamentary capacity. The patient demonstrated intact functioning on a dementia screen and overall intact cognitive functioning. There were isolated cognitive deficits, but they did not suggest a dementing process and should not interfere with the patient's ability to prepare a will. There was also no evidence of psychiatric problems sufficient to interfere with the patient's testamentary capacity.

Driving Capacity

Introduction

Regarding Americans and driving, Marshall McLuhan in 1964 said, "The car has become an article of dress without which we feel uncertain, unclad, and incomplete" (McLuhan, 1964). As this quote indicates, driving is a central and longstanding characteristic of American culture. On average, nationwide, drivers learner's permits are allowed starting at age 14 with a provisional license by age 16, followed with a full license by age 18. Once a full license is attained the Department of Motor Vehicles (DMV),[2] or other designated state motor vehicle department, does not take away an individual's drivers license upon reaching a certain age. Although there is variability across states in older driver re-licensing laws, the license to drive is generally dependent on a person's mental and/or physical condition and ability to follow traffic laws and rules, regardless of age. (http://www.agingsociety.org/agingsociety/links/driverLicense.html).

A person's cognitive and physical ability to drive is usually questioned when there is a recent history of a stroke, brain injury, presence of a progressive dementia, history of increased citations, and development of epilepsy or other neurological conditions that could negatively affect driving ability. For instance, in California, a reexamination of driving ability can be prompted by reports made by professionals, such as physicians, emergency technicians, and peace officers who become aware of an individual having a physical or mental condition associated with loss of consciousness or control or behaviors suggestive of unsafe driving.

Laws vary by state in terms of who can make a report. In some states physicians and surgeons are required to notify the state's motor vehicle department of certain conditions and disorders, and it is up to their discretion to report other conditions that could impact an individual's ability to drive. In other states, health care providers are not allowed to contact state agencies with private health information. Whether or not psychologists are mandated or allowed reporters also will vary from state to state. In most states, family and peers can file reports to the state motor vehicle department if they believe that a person is no longer safe to drive. In summary, some state motor vehicle departments allow for both professionals and non-professionals to notify them of individuals whose driving privileges need to be reexamined. It is up to the discretion of the DMV or other designated state motor vehicle department to determine what action will be taken. Readers are referred to their state DMV for further information on notification process and regulations.

Increasingly, psychologists are being asked to partake in the evaluation of an older individual's capacity to drive and to assess the various components that contribute to driving. The license to drive is dependent on both physical and mental abilities that affect the ability to follow traffic laws and rules. Therefore, an evaluation should assess: (1) a person's physical ability to drive; (2) cognitive ability to understand not just driving rules, but how to properly drive a car; (3) cognitive ability to implement knowledge of driving-related information; and (4) psychiatric, substance use, and emotional factors that contribute to driving. It is essential to know if an individual has a history of risk-taking behavior, aggressive driving, and use of drugs or medications that could affect driving (Schultheis, 2007). Additionally, anxiety about driving, as well as overconfidence in one's driving abilities can impact driving capacity. Ideally, a comprehensive driving evaluation should include a medical evaluation, complete psychological evaluation, and driver specialist evaluation.

A psychologists role may vary depending on the setting. A psychologist may make a recommendation after reviewing the driver

---

[2] States differ in the name of the agency that regulates driving. In this handbook the term "Department of Motor Vehicles" or "DMV" will be used to apply to any such state agency.

specialist evaluation, or the driver specialist may make a recommendation after reviewing the psychological test results, or a physician may utilize both the psychological test results and the driver specialist evaluation results to provide a recommendation.

Legal Elements/Standards

Capacity to drive a motor vehicle and grounds for revoking the privilege are established by state motor vehicle laws. While variations in the law are common, the Uniform Vehicle Code provides a fairly representative norm. It provides that no license shall be issued when the commissioner has good cause to believe that a person "by reason of physical or mental disability would not be able to operate a motor vehicle with safety upon the highways" (National Committee on Uniform Traffic Laws and Ordinances, 2000).

The tremendous variety of physical, mental, and emotional impairments that can result in an inability to operate a motor vehicle safely results in substantial assessment variability, but regardless of the nature or source of impairment, the legal standard ultimately looks at its practical impact on the individual's ability to operate a motor vehicle with reasonable and ordinary control.

Functional Elements of Driving Capacity

Driving capacity involves more than a person's knowledge about driving and cognitive abilities to participate in the driving task, but also the individual's ability to participate in driving despite potential physical frailty or other limited abilities.

1. Visual Acuity

Has it become difficult for the person to read signs, estimate distance, or differentiate a pole from a person standing at the intersection preparing to cross? Visual acuity is necessary in order to be able to navigate and not get lost, to be aware of changes in one's route (e.g., detours, construction, etc.), to be aware of speed signs, and to discern a safe from a dangerous driving situation. Additionally, functional visual field

declines with age and has been found to correlate with crash data in older drivers (Owsley et al., 1998). Clearly, visual acuity plays an essential role in driving capacity. Psychologists should therefore inquire about last eye examination, medical conditions that could affect vision (e.g., diabetes), and refer to an eye clinic if necessary.

2. Flexibility and Strength

Injuries, decreased activity, and various medical conditions (e.g., arthritis) could potentially affect a person's flexibility and strength. Neck and shoulder pain or lack of flexibility could limit a driver's ability to swivel and glance over their shoulder to quickly check their blind spot before changing lanes. Decreased strength or sensation in hands could change a driver's ability to hold onto and control the steering wheel considerably during both routine and emergency driving situations. Decreased sensation, strength, and coordination in legs and feet could potentially result in difficulties using the brakes, the accelerator, and the clutch, especially during unexpected situations.

3. Reaction Time

Reaction time is known to slow with age and may impact driving abilities. For example, reaction time can impact driving by slowing response time when faced with an expected situation (e.g., a ball rolling out in front of the car), to determine what the necessary driving response should be (e.g., brake, swerve, slow down), to plan the action (e.g., step on brake, turn steering wheel, take right foot off of the accelerator), and to implement it. Changes in visual acuity, flexibility, strength, as well as normal changes in processing speed associated with aging will all affect a driver's reaction time. Older adults with mobility issues or certain neurological conditions are at heightened risk for slowed reaction time.

4. Knowledge

An individual needs to demonstrate knowledge of the rules of the road and the potential consequences of not obeying the rules (e.g., tickets, incarceration, and injury to self or others). A driver should be able to demonstrate knowledge of basic automobile functions and what to do in emergent situations (e.g., driving in rain versus snow, which way to turn in a skid, why is tire pressure important).

5. Appreciation of Medical Diagnosis

An individual needs to appreciate how medial conditions may impact driving ability. The person should be able to identify, if viable, potential ways to safely compensate for foreseeable weaknesses.

6. Judgment

A driver needs to demonstrate judgment in driving situations. Ascertaining abilities to handle hypothetical situations, such as "What would he or she do if there was a flat tire? How does he or she handle frustration while on the road and that of other drivers?" may yield helpful insights.

7. Driving Efficacy

Assessing the person's level of confidence in his or her own driving ability can provide valuable information regarding functional driving capacity. One might ask about confidence level in terms of vision in the day or night, comfort with freeway driving, strength and ability to make sharp turns, and/or to respond to situations requiring a rapid response.

Diagnostic Considerations

Various medical conditions could potentially affect driving ability. These include, but are not limited to: musculoskeletal disorders, sensory disorders, arthritis, dementia, psychiatric disorders, stroke, sleep apnea, and substance use. Dementia, for instance, can impair memory, as well as attention, visual spatial abilities, language abilities, and judgment. Additionally, medical conditions that are associated with abrupt changes in cognition, such as epilepsy, diabetes, or heart disease, can place an individual at higher risk for a motor vehicle accident (Waller, 1980). A close review of medications is critical as many prescription drugs can be sedating and impair driving ability. Medications known to impair driving include: opioids, benzodiazepines, antidepressants, hypnotics, antipsychotics, antihistamines, glaucoma agents, nonsteroidal anti-inflammatory drugs, and muscle relaxants (Carr, 2000). Medical and psychological diagnosis, along with medications used to treat these conditions, need to be a component of the driving capacity evaluation, but do not necessarily automatically negate an individual's ability to drive.

Cognitive Underpinnings

There is a well-developed domain of research to draw upon in terms of cognitive underpinnings of driving abilities. Consistent evidence has supported the notion that driving performance in older adults is related to visual attention and processing speed (Lee, Lee, & Cameron, 2003; Roenker, Cissell, Ball, Wadley, & Edwards, 2003). Changes in functional visual field, that area from which a person can attain visual information in a quick glance (Sanders, 1970) has received particular interest. The useful-field-of-view (UFOV) test is a measure commonly used to assess functional visual field by testing visual processing speed and visual attention during higher order processing tasks. Studies have found a relationship between performance on UFOV tests and future at-fault motor vehicle accidents (Owsley et al., 1998; Ball et al., 2006). The size of the functional visual field has been found to be affected by visual sensory function, delays in processing ability, difficulties with divided attention, and inability to ignore distracters (Owsley, Ball, & Keeton, 1995; Ball, Roenkel, & Bruni, 1990). It is therefore considered a key cognitive component to driving ability.

Other important cognitive mechanisms associated with driving difficulties include impaired memory, impaired visual acuity, decline in peripheral vision, and decreased ability to perform two tasks simultaneously (McGwin, Chapman, & Owsley, 2000; Bravo & Nakayama, 1992; McPeek & Nakayama, 1995).

Cognitive abilities can be negatively impacted by substance abuse, as well as a variety of medical conditions and medications, and the impairments can range from mild to severe, and can be progressive, permanent, or reversible (e.g., medication side-effects). It is therefore essential to assess cognition and attain a thorough history to identify potential variables that could be impacting cognitive abilities associated to driving.

Psychiatric and Emotional Factors

There are various psychiatric and emotional factors that can affect driving abilities. Symptoms related to psychosis, such as delusions, hallucinations, and disorganized thinking, can potentially lead to risky driving behavior due to the person misinterpreting their environment and behaving erratically. Anxiety and medications to treat anxiety can both influence a person's physical and mental ability to drive. For instance, anxiety can increase muscle tension, distort the environmental data that the driver attends to, and lead to poor decisions regarding necessary driving maneuvers (e.g., I am in the far left lane and I need to make a right turn on this street?). Medications for anxiety can cause a dangerous level of muscle relaxation that can impede the ability to drive or cause sedation. Depression can lead to fatigue, decreased sleep, and problems focusing and making decisions, all of which can have negative effects on driving ability. Additionally, being sleep deprived can lead to increased risk for motor vehicle accidents due to drowsiness. Medications to address sleep deprivation may also negatively affect driving ability if taken incorrectly.

Abuse of prescription and non-prescription drugs may go undetected. Pain medicine, for instance, can be abused and influence driving ability. Use of amphetamines or other stimulants should also be considered. The abuse of alcohol is obviously a major concern for driving. Older adults are more likely to be on prescription medications and if these are combined with alcohol it could alter cognition and increase the effects of alcohol to a greater degree than drinking alcohol alone, making driving more dangerous. The effects of long-term heavy alcohol use, such as cerebellar degeneration, polyneuropathy, amblyopia, and alcohol dementia, can begin to develop or become intensified, and gradually increase impairments in driving. Clearly, a thorough assessment of mental health problems and substance use is necessary to identify potential driving complications.

Values

Society's value on driving and independence can cloud not just the adult's judgment but that of the clinician who is trying to be benevolent. From a psychological perspective driving represents independence and vitality. Socially, an individual that drives has a broader scope of social and financial resources, and can be more active in the community. Driving can be a source of self-esteem, as people may equate the need to be driven to being a burden or being useless. For some, the inability to drive can be perceived as an enormous loss in life and can greatly influence their view of self and can lead to increased mental health problems (Marottoli et al., 1997).

Driving cessation in older adults has been associated with depression and diminished out-of-home activities, as well as increased caregiver stress (Foley, Harley, Heimovitz, Guralnik, & Brock, 2002; Marottoli et al., 1997; Marottoli et al. 2000; Azad, Byszewksi, Amos, & Molnar, 2002). Individuals who have to stop driving report that an inability to participate in leisure activities is the domain most impacted by loss of the driver's license (Azad et al., 2002). It is therefore important for clinicians to monitor a person's reaction and identify sources of support if driving abilities are suspended. Working with the adult and the family or friends (if available) to identify feasible transportation options is essential in order to decrease caregiver burden and to promote as much continued independence for the adult as possible.

The value placed on driving will also depend on where the individual lives. Communities vary, and those individuals who live in areas with good public transportation may be more comfortable with the idea of giving up driving than someone who is completely reliant on their car for everyday necessities and socializing.

A number of technologies may support older adults who continue to drive. These developments may include automatic braking systems to minimize unnecessary accelerating, navigation systems, climate controls to keep the driver alert, and a system that goes beyond the car by using a Global Positioning System (GPS) with an Intelligent Transportation System (ITS) to send information to vehicles when a pedestrian is nearby. Driving safety must be evaluated within the context of the owner's current vehicle.

Notably, many older drivers show concern and insight into driving habits and self regulate by driving only during the daytime, driving slower, or limiting driving to shorter or non-highway distances. Actively involving the elderly adult in planning for future driving limitations and cessation may help to reduce the negative effects that a sudden and mandatory loss of driving privilege could have. For more information on advance care planning for driving changes see the Alzheimer's Association Web site at: http://www.alz.org/living_with_-alzheimers_driving.asp

Risks

An example of the grave social and personal dangers that at-risk drivers pose is the July 16, 2003, case in Santa Monica, California, in which an 87-year-old driver drove his car into a crowded farmer's market, killing 10 people and injuring 63 more. Police investigations indicated that the driver hit the gas pedal instead of the brake and that the car was actually stopped by the body of a victim that was trapped underneath the car (www.cnn.com/2004/-LAW/01/05/farmer.market.crash).

Drivers age 16-20, followed by those age 21-34, have the highest rates of traffic fatalities. As a group, drivers age 65 and older drive fewer miles than other age groups, but pose the next greater risk for injury or fatality in motor vehicle accidents. Among older adults, the risk for driving injury and fatality increases with age.

Dellinger, Sehgal, Sleet, and Barrett-Connor (2001) found that among elderly drivers who had stopped driving within the past five years, the majority did it for medical reasons. Interestingly, however, those who stopped driving had fewer medical problems than those who continued to drive, suggesting that accumulation of medical problems alone is not the determining factor in the decision to stop driving and that perhaps overall health or functional ability played a greater role in the decision. Okonkwo, Crowe, Wadley, Ball (2008) examined self-regulation of driving for older adults with varying functional abilities and found that a significant portion of high-risk drivers did not restrict their driving. Their findings point to the probability that for many older individuals, the value of driving outweighs the potential risks of unsafe driving due to decreased functional abilities.

Clearly, there are many variables that go into the life-altering decision to stop driving. The significant benefits and risks of continued versus cessation of driving need to be well thought-out when considering a decision to limit or stop driving for older adults who are experiencing medical, physical, and functional declines that are adversely affecting driving.

Steps to Enhance Driving Capacity

Several options are available for individuals who present with limited driving capacity. For instance, if the concern is primarily physical limitations due to hemiplegia or weakness, a car can be modified to accommodate the driver (e.g., creating a left foot accelerator or a car that can be driven with just the use of one's hands). A review of treatable or reversible conditions affecting driving capacity, such as a mood disorder or medications, should also be conducted. Another possibility is to limit the license to driving a certain route or only under certain conditions. In some cases, extended driver's training with a Driver Rehabilitation Specialist (DRS) or refresher courses for older drivers (e.g., AARP Driver Safety Program, http://www.aarp.org/families/driver_safety/) may also be an option. Studies have found also that training in speed-of-processing, as assessed by the useful-field-of-view (UFOV) test, correlated with improvements in driving on simulator measures and during driving evaluation (Roenker et al., 2003).

Clinical Judgment of Driving Capacity

Clinical judgment of driving capacity will include the safety of the driver and the community, as well as the psychological benefits and risks of permanent loss of driver's license and/or continued driving. Clinical judgment may include consideration as to whether the individual needs to stop driving immediately or perhaps helping the person prepare for an eventual transition from driver to non-driver. There may be times when findings from a psychological evaluation clearly indicate impairment in all or most cognitive areas essential to driving. In this case, the psychologist can recommend to the physician and DRS that driving not be pursued. However, on other occasions a clinician may recommend that the physician and the DRS team proceed with caution, gather more data, or discourage the adult from pursuing driving. The clinician needs to keep in mind that the purpose of the psychological component of the evaluation is not to absolutely determine driving capacity, but to provide input and recommendations to the physician and DRS.

Clinical Approaches to Assessing Driving Capacity

A comprehensive assessment of driving capacity can be composed of three parts: medical exam, psychological evaluation, and driving evaluation. The use of stand alone psychological testing is not recommended to determine driving capacity. Psychologists should make every effort to collaborate with physicians and driver specialists whenever participating in a driving capacity evaluation.

Medical Exam

The first step in a driving capacity evaluation should be a medical exam. This is necessary to rule out potential medical conditions that could impair driving ability. In most states physicians are legally mandated to report cases that involve medical conditions that could affect driving. Therefore, a prior report regarding the examinee's questionable driving ability due to a medical condition may already be documented. In the DMV's reexamination process, an individual can be asked to present medical information related to their driving ability and should therefore be prepared to

present medical documentation supporting their desire to re-instate a license to drive.

Psychological Evaluation

The purpose of the psychological evaluation is to enhance the physician and driver specialists' knowledge of the adult's cognitive and emotional functioning and how these may detrimentally affect driving ability. This information can be used to identify areas of strength and weakness that can also be useful if the adult is referred for driver's training. A psychological evaluation can consist of a clinical interview, cognitive measures, and personality/behavioral measures.

Clinical Interview: The clinical interview will help to establish rapport and can be used to gather information related to the adult's premorbid driving style, history of driving citations, and their awareness of current medical and physical circumstances that could affect their driving ability. The clinical interview can be used to gather information on how the adult anticipates how he or she will resolve unexpected driving situations.

During the clinical interview gathering information from available family and friends can also shed light on the adult's driving habits. Although collateral information is important, the clinician needs to keep in mind that it can also be biased and that occasionally family and friends may underreport or misinterpret the adult's driving behaviors (Hunt, 1993).

Personality/Behavioral Measures: Assessing anxiety and depression is important as these are treatable conditions that can contribute to delayed responses, distraction, and errors when driving. These can be assessed, for instance, with the Beck Depression Inventory, Beck Anxiety Inventory, and Geriatric Depression Scale.

Cognitive Measures: A psychological battery for assessing driving capacity may include measures to assess mental status, attention, working memory, divided attention, information processing speed, executive functions, visual spatial abilities, visual perception, inhibition, and language. Tests of visuospatial abilities are the most related to different driving measures (Reger, Welsh, Watson, Cholerton, Baker, & Craft, 2004).

Psychological batteries that serve as a component of an evaluation of driving capacity may include a wide range of instruments depending upon the particulars of the referral. Some examples include: Mini Mental State Examination; Dementia Rating Scale; Trail Making Test Parts A and B; Cancellation Task; WAIS Digit Symbol, Digit Span, Information, Picture Arrangement, and Block Design subtests; Simple or Choice/Complex Reaction Time; Motor-Free Visual Perceptual Test; PASAT; WASI Matrix Reasoning; WMS-III Logical Memory, Facial Recognition, Visual Reproduction subtests; Benton Visual Retention Test; RBANS; Stroop; Rey-Complex Figure; Word Fluency; Boston Naming Test; Porteous Maze; Right/Left Orientation; Cognistat; Independent Living Scale; and Driving Judgment Situations (Reger et al., 2004; Schultheis, 2007; Pasino & Kahan, 2001).

Specialized Driving Tests: Other measures that are more specialized for assessment of driving include Cognitive Behavioral Driving Test, DriveABLE Screen, and Useful Field of View (UFOV), a measure of processing speed and spatial attention used to predict driving performance (Schultheis, 2007). Performance on these cognitive measures can provide useful information regarding a person's ability to visually scan and track information, to attend to the driving task, to shift set/multitask, to problem solve, and to reason through driving situations.

It should be noted that correlations between neuropsychological tests and on-road tests are variable (Reger et al., 2004; Schultheis, 2007) so although the results of psychological cognitive testing is important, it is essential to keep in mind that their ability to predict actual driving ability is limited.

Another limitation to the application of psychological measures in assessing ability to drive is that there is no well-defined appropriate cut off for driving (Reger et al., 2004). Unless an individual displays a significant impairment (e.g., left visual field cut or neglect), it is left up to clinical judgment to determine how poorly and on what measures an individual can perform

in order to support or not support the re-instatement of a driver's license.

In essence, psychological testing can assess various components of driving, but correlations between test results and driving are not well established, cut off scores that predict impaired driving are not standardized, and psychological testing does not test all of the abilities required for driving simultaneously in an in vivo situation. Therefore, it is not recommended that they be the sole determining factor in assessing an individual's ability to drive.

Driver Specialist Evaluation

The final component of a thorough driving capacity evaluation is the driver specialist evaluation. This entails evaluating the examinee's actual driving ability through virtual driving tests, as well as behind the wheel testing. The Association for Driver Rehabilitation Specialists (ADED) has a national listing of agencies offering driving evaluations that can be viewed online at www.driver-ed.org, or contact them toll free at 1-800-290-2344. Driver Rehabilitation Specialists (DRS) must meet certain requirements and are generally licensed kinesthesiologists, licensed occupational therapists, registered physical therapists, or state approved driving instructors or driver education teachers. The purpose of their evaluation is to determine current level of driving ability and, under certain circumstances, to determine if driver training or classroom education would be beneficial (NMEDA & ADED Model Practices for Driver Rehabilitation for Individuals with Disabilities, May 2002). Findings from a psychological evaluation can be useful during this component of the driving capacity evaluation because it can provide information to the DRS regarding strengths and weaknesses of the potential driver.

Case Examples

The following two cases were selected to demonstrate the possible variability in psychological testing and how findings can be communicated to drivers' training programs and physicians. Both individuals were referred by their physician for neuropsychological testing and a driver's evaluation, if appropriate, to assess driving ability and for driving recommendations. They were both seeking to re-instate their driver's license after sustaining a brain injury that led to a physician report to the DMV.

Case 1

Psychology Component

Case 1 is a 65-year-old female diagnosed with traumatic brain injury, seizure disorder, and depression with history of alcohol and drug abuse. She was evaluated for driving capacity 18 months after discharge from an inpatient hospital. Psychological testing revealed the following:

Test	Observed Performance
MMSE	Average
Trails A	Impaired
Trails B	Impaired
RBANS:	
Immediate Memory	Low Average
Visual Construction	Average
Language	Average
Attention	Borderline
Delayed Memory	Low Average
Total Test RBANS	Low Average
WASI Matrix Reasoning	Borderline
NCSE Abstract Reasoning	Average
ILS Health & Safety	Mild Impairment
Driving Judgment Situations	Average

In terms of Neurobehavioral Functioning she showed none to little: faulty orientation, disinhibition, impaired initiation, agitation/irritability, behavior dyscontrol, blunted affect, emotional lability, bizarre thinking, inaccurate insight, or suicidality. She demonstrated borderline fatigability, anxiety, and depression.

The psychological evaluation resulted in diagnosis of Alcohol Abuse and Cognitive Disorder, NOS. In the discussion, significant difficulties with visual scanning and shifting set were noted, as well as mild difficulties with problem solving. Longstanding and probable ongoing alcohol abuse was considered to be contributing to her current testing profile.

Caution in pursuing driving was recommended due to cognitive issues.

Driver Specialist Component

Her clinical driving evaluation was conducted 14 months after the psychological evaluation. A specially trained occupational therapist conducted the evaluation. It consisted of gathering history regarding her health and medications, identifying her driving goals, driving history, vehicle she was interested in driving, mobility factors, assessing cognition, as well as evaluating her vision, perception, and physical status. The evaluation also looked at activities of daily living status, current transportation, and wheelchair necessity. It assessed variables related to communication and behaviors that could influence her readiness to drive.

Under medical history, it was noted she had a history of seizure disorder, brain injury, left sided weakness, depression, and alcohol use. It was indicated she reported not using alcohol in 12 months and being seizure free for 18 months. Use of an antidepressant, anticonvulsant, and pain medication was noted. In regards to her activities of daily living it was stated she was independent with all self care tasks. She did not use a wheelchair and was independent for all mobility. Factors that were identified as influencing her readiness to drive included physical limitations, psychosocial factors, cognitive limitations, and difficulty following multiple directions.

Under vision, it was noted that she required corrective lenses for driving but not for reading. Her peripheral vision was intact. Occulomotor convergence was normal. Occulomotor range of motion was full range with jerky tracking for both eyes. Perception tests identified left-right confusion. In assessing her physical ability of upper and lower extremities to drive a car (i.e., proprioception, strength, range of motion, motor control, and tone), she performed within normal limits, except for motor control of lower extremities which was rated as limited. Range of motion for her neck was within normal limits. On tests of right foot reaction time for simple (i.e., red and green) and complex (i.e., green, yellow, and red) scenarios, she demonstrated overshooting and hesitation.

The findings of the DRS determined that she had questionable driving potential and a recommendation of 6 driving lessons was made. Concerns included delayed visual processing, frequent need for repetition of instructions, decreased smooth coordinated control of lower extremities, and overshooting and delayed reaction time of right foot.

During the driving simulation she demonstrated good control of the vehicle but was unable to find her way back to the training site and was unable to consistently follow rules of the road. Only three driving lessons were completed due to the driver demonstrating problems with short-term memory and visual processing. The final recommendation was that she not drive.

Case 2

Psychology Component

Case 2 is a 68-year-old male who, at time of discharge, was diagnosed with traumatic brain injury, high blood pressure, and dislocation of the left shoulder. He was evaluated six months after discharge from an inpatient hospital. History was positive for cocaine use, but he had not used any substances for over five years. Psychological testing revealed the following:

Test	Observed Performance
MMSE	Average
Trails A	Average
Trails B	Average
RBANS:	
Immediate Memory	Average
Visual Construction	Average
Language	Average
Attention	Borderline
Delayed Memory	Average
Total Test RBANS	Low Average
WASI Matrix Reasoning	Average
NCSE Abstract Reasoning	Average
ILS Health & Safety	Average
Driving Judgment Situations	Average

In terms of neurobehavioral functioning he showed none to little: faulty orientation, disinhibition, impaired initiation, agitation/irritability, behavior dyscontrol, blunted affect, emotional lability, fatigability, bizarre thinking, inaccurate insight, or suicidality. He demonstrated borderline anxiety and depression.

The psychological evaluation resulted in a diagnosis of status post traumatic brain injury with improving cognitive status. The findings indicated average functioning, with presence of anxiety and low mood related to changes in work status that was affecting his attention. He was described as missing details, but noted to be generally cognitively intact and the recommendation was to proceed with drivers training.

Driver Specialist Component

His clinical driving evaluation was conducted by a specially trained occupational therapist. It consisted of gathering of history regarding his health and medications, identifying adult's driving goal, driving history, vehicle he was interested in driving, mobility factors, assessing cognition, as well as evaluating his vision, perception, and physical status. The evaluation also looked at activities of daily living status, current transportation, and wheelchair necessity. It assessed variables related to communication and behaviors that could influence his readiness to drive.

Under vision, it was noted he required corrective lenses for reading but not for driving. His peripheral vision was intact for both eyes. Occulomotor convergence was normal. Occulomotor range of motion was full range for both eyes with slight ptosis and slightly ectopic right eye being identified. Perception tests were normal. In assessing his physical ability to drive a car, limited gross strength and limited range of motion of left shoulder was noted. Range of motion for his neck, as well as upper extremity and lower extremity functions were within normal limits. His reaction time for right foot was measured for simple (i.e., red and green) and complex (i.e., green, yellow, and red) scenarios, and was deemed to be satisfactory.

During the driving simulation he was assessed in the program car with modified equipment. He demonstrated good control of the vehicle and good safety habits. He was able to adjust the speed of the car and its position even when at freeway speeds.

Overall the driving specialist evaluation found him to have adequate visual processing, good problem solving for driving scenarios, good reaction time, and mild difficulty with information retrieval. The recommendation was that he be referred to the DMV for a formal road test. Shortly thereafter he was formally cleared medically for driving and a formal notification was given to the DMV.

Conclusion

A driving capacity evaluation entails a collaborative effort between physicians, psychologists, and DRS. Although driving itself can become a routine and over-learned activity, the fact is that the environment in which it occurs is fluid and with limited predictability. The foundation for driving is physical: a driver needs to have sufficient physical ability to maneuver an automobile, not just during routine daily driving, but also in sudden, unexpected situations. The next step is brain function and emotional state. A driver needs to recall and use good judgment, not just about day-to-day rules of the road, but about unusual circumstances that can arise. Anxiety, depression, anger, prescription and non-prescription drugs, and cognitive impairments can all influence physical reactions and driving judgment, particularly in unanticipated conditions. And finally, the product is the integration of physical ability, cognitive ability, and emotional state into an actual safe driving experience in both mundane and unexpected driving conditions. As the American population ages, psychologists' involvement in driving capacity evaluations is likely to increase and it will be important to be aware of what the assessment entails and to collaborate with other professionals in order to ensure both the safety of older adults and other drivers on the road.

Independent Living

Introduction

In much of the dominant American culture, adulthood is often marked by an individual's ability to move out of a parent's home and live independently. A person who lives on his or her own is thought of as self-sufficient, accountable for one's own welfare, and worthy to enjoy a certain degree of freedom within the home. Illness and financial circumstances, however, can interfere with a person's ability to live independently. The need for functional support may increase as people age, due to functional limitations associated with physical ailments that may accompany aging. Familiarity with a neighborhood or environment may become more important for safety and socialization, and the cultural emphasis on self-autonomy may result in a concern for becoming a burden to others.

The development of a medical illness that results in changes in a person's ability to care for him or herself can lead to hospitalization. A gradual decline in physical abilities can eventually limit a person from being able to perform activities of daily living (ADLs) necessary for survival, as well as instrumental activities of daily living (IADLs) (i.e., management of healthcare, finances, the home, etc.). The same is true for the development of memory problems that can lead a person to forget about soup on the stove, to take medication, or how to get to the grocery store and back. The development or exacerbation of mental health problems related to a thought disorder or mood disorder can also affect a person's ability to live independently. An individual can become homeless for many reasons, including mental health problems, substance abuse issues, and cognitive deficits. In general, when a person's ability to care for him or herself comes into question, an evaluation to determine independent living capacity should be considered.

Evaluations for capacity to determine independent living are often done by psychologists. They may be the sole evaluator or part of a team of professionals. These assessments use various measures to determine cognitive abilities, decision-making abilities, physical/functional abilities, and whether or not the factors are reversible. In some cases, these evaluations are done in the context of determining whether the individual needs a guardian of person. In other cases, these evaluations remain in more of a clinical realm, focusing on helping to determine the appropriate discharge location that matches the person's needs. In any case, these evaluations are often among the most difficult because they concern such a fundamental value—independence—and because the range of skills and abilities that are potentially relevant is so vast.

Legal Elements/Standards

In most states, there is unlikely to be a specific standard for "the capacity to live independently." Instead, the most relevant legal standards for the capacity to live independently are likely those which are defined in guardianship law. In Chapter 2, it was noted that state statutes for incapacity under guardianship vary widely, but that many cite one or more of four "tests":

1. The presence of a disabling condition;
2. A functional element—sometimes defined as the inability to meet essential needs to live independently;
3. A problem with cognition;
4. A necessity component—that is that guardianship is necessary because less restrictive alternatives have failed.

A list of such less restrictive alternatives is provided in Appendix F.

As an example, the Uniform Guardianship and Protective Proceedings Act (UGPPA; a model act that states may use when revising guardianship statutes) defines an incapacitated individual as someone who is unable to receive and evaluate information or make or communicate decisions [*cognitive element*] to the extent that the individual lacks the ability to meet essential requirements for physical health, safety, or self-care [*functional element*], even with appropriate technological assistance [*necessity element*] [bracketed notes added] (National Conference of Commissioners on Uniform State Laws, 1997).

The most recent UGPPA standard does not include diagnostic or causal elements, although most state statutes do. The framework of this handbook includes a diagnostic component because it establishes the causal condition behind the functional deficits, and informs the choice of treatments, the course of the disorder, and the prognosis for improvement.

In some states, legal guidance relevant to independent living may be provided in the adult protective services (APS) statutes. Some psychologists may be familiar with these as the statutes that define "elder abuse" or "adult abuse" and address reporting to APS, whether mandatory or voluntary. Adult protective services investigates allegations of elder or adult abuse and provides services to individuals that are at risk for abuse, neglect, or exploitation. Recently the ABA Commission on Law and Aging analyzed all state laws and concluded that the threshold criteria for APS intervention can be organized into the following five categories: age, condition, function, living situation, and services received. Each of these categories incorporates an array of concepts. The ABA Commission has grouped the diverse statutory terminology into subcategories. For example, the APS statutes that have a "condition" criterion may refer to these subcategories: mental or physical impairment, mental or physical illness, dementia, or substance abuse. The APS statutes that have a "function" criterion include these subcategories:

1. Lacking the ability to make, communicate, or implement decisions.

2. Lacking the ability to understand the risks and consequences of behavior.
3. Being dependent on others.
4. Requiring care, treatment, or custody for own welfare or welfare of others.
5. Restricted ability to carry out ADLs.
6. Unable to care for or manage ones' self or property.
7. Unable to delegate responsibility.
8. Unable to perform or obtain services.
9. Unable to protect self.

An individual who is living independently but who is determined to be unable to care for him or herself may be self-neglecting. While the complicated and evolving concept of self-neglect is beyond the scope of this handbook, it is important that psychologists are aware that many APS laws address self-neglect, and that a report to APS about a self-neglecting individual may be required by state law or, even if not required, may be appropriate under the circumstances. A report to APS may result in additional interventions, monitoring, or support for the individual.

For further information, readers are encouraged see the ABA Commission's analysis of state APS laws by visiting its Web site at www.abanet.org/aging.

In summary, in preparing to evaluate capacity to live independently, familiarity with guardianship statutes, APS statutes, and other law related to the capacity to live independently and, broadly, to care for one's person is important. However, such law and legal guidance regarding the task of living independently can be so broad that they may not provide much specific direction to the psychologist.

In this handbook we propose that a psychological evaluation relevant to the capacity to live independently needs to determine if an individual is a significant danger to her or himself due to limited functional abilities, or due to cognitive or psychiatric disturbances, and also cannot accept or appropriately use assistance that would allow him or her to live independently. These functional, cognitive, and psychiatric issues are further detailed in the next sections.

Functional Element

A common framework in gerontologic literature for everyday functioning is the ADL/IADL framework. There is no exact agreement on the specific areas considered ADLs and IADLs—but generally the ADLs are "basic" to personal care (eating, bathing, toileting, etc.), whereas the IADLs are "higher level" abilities, such as financial management, household management. As described in Appendix B, there are a number of useful tests for rating ADLs and IADLs.

An assessment of ADLs and IADLs, however, is insufficient to evaluate the capacity to live independently, because it is more of a categorization of important activities, and does not consider the cognitive and judgment skills related to these. In a seminal survey of clinical and legal professionals involved in guardianship, key abilities essential to independent living were defined and q-sorted (Anderten, 1979). A number ADLs/IADLs were identified (such as diet, hygiene, maintain household, use transportation), but also key judgmental abilities (such as the ability to handle emergencies and compensate for deficits). This emphasis on cognition is also reflected in another study that aimed to identify the key functional elements for independent living under guardianship using a social cognitive framework (Anderer, 1997). In this framework, the key judgmental factors are the ability to identify a problem, generate alternative solutions, make the decision, implement the solutions, and verify the solution.

In this handbook, we propose a three-part framework for the functional elements associated with independent living. This framework was developed from consideration of the above cited studies, as well as from a rehabilitation perspective in which the goal is for individuals to be as independent as possible despite limited physical and cognitive abilities. We propose that the assessment of capacity to live independently, therefore, requires the integration of understanding what is required to live independently, the functional ability to apply one's knowledge ("application"), and the ability to problem solve and appreciate consequences of potential choices ("judgment").

This framework reflects legal standards found in guardianship laws that emphasize cognitive and functional components, as well as cognitive, functional, and judgmental components of independent living cited in APS laws. It allows the clinician to conceptualize and evaluate how cognitive factors, physical deficits, and maladaptive behaviors could be interfering with the patient's ability to live on their own.

1. Understanding

Does the adult understand the day-to-day requirements of taking care of self and home? For instance, does he understand that bills need to be paid in order to keep utilities running? Does she know how much their income consists of and does she keep track of banking to ensure checks do not bounce? Does he understand that grocery shopping needs to be done regularly in order to have sufficient food in the house? Is she aware of kitchen safety to prevent fires? Does he understand weekly chores versus daily chores? Does she understand how their medical problems may affect the ability to maintain a home and health? In general, what is the adult's understanding of the basic requirements necessary to live independently and can he or she foresee possible problems related to performing or not performing tasks?

2. Application

If the adult has an understanding of general requirements of living independently, is the individual able to either perform the tasks required for managing home and health or direct another person to assist them? For example, an adult with history of stroke with residual right-sided hemiplegia may not be able to write checks necessary for paying bills, but can this person direct someone to do it and to balance the checkbook? Can the person clean the kitchen and dishes sufficiently to prevent contamination of food by bacteria and/or pests? If there are pets, does the individual feed and clean up after them? How does the person maintain personal hygiene? In essence, are there physical or cognitive limitations and if so can the adult problem solve around them in order to continue to maintain health and the home?

In general an assessment of the person's ability to perform activities of daily living, such as dressing themselves, toileting, bathing, transferring, and mobility, is essential. Difficulties in any of these areas can potentially lead to deterioration of the individual's hygiene, health, and self-esteem. What is more key, however, is not if the person can or cannot do the task, but if not, does the person recognize the need to have the task done (insight), and will he or she accept help for that need?

3. Judgment

Does the presence of a cognitive disorder, emotional disorder, or thought disorder affect the person's judgment as it relates to care of self or the home? In some cases an individual may understand the requirements for independent living, and be willing to do those or accept help for those, but exercise poor judgment in doing those consistently, in avoiding high-risk behaviors when alone, or in responding to emergency situations that arise. An example of when this would become a concern follows: a woman suffers from depression and therefore experiences depressed mood, anhedonia, decreased motivation, poor appetite, and hypersomnia. Her symptoms prevent her from "caring" about her health and her home and she is, therefore, not motivated to perform the tasks herself or to seek assistance from someone else. In this case, her ability to functionally care for herself and her home and to live independently is severely affected by an emotional disorder. She may not be able to accurately foresee the potential consequences of not performing day-to-day tasks related to her personal survival and her home.

Diagnostic Considerations

In older adults, the most common disorder likely to affect the capacity to live independently is dementia. Innumerable studies have documented the relationship between the severity of dementia and the performance of functional abilities key to independent living (Tatemichi, Desmond, Stern, Paik, & Bagiella, 1994; Hill, Backman & Fatiglioni, 1995).

The best symptom predictors of institutionalization of individuals with dementia have been excessive night-time activity, immobility or difficulty walking, and incontinence (Hope, Keene, Gedling, Fairburn, & Jacoby, 1999), along with caregiver factors. For example, institutionalization of a cognitively impaired older adult is less likely to occur when the caregiver is provided respite through family assistance with overnight help and ADLs (Gaugler et al., 2000). While dementia is the greatest risk factor for institutionalization of older adults, medical burden was the most salient variable for non-demented older persons (Bharucha, Panday, Shen, Dodge, & Ganguli, 2004).

In addition to cognitive impairments, other factors identified in the literature that are associated with decline in functional status in older adults who live in the community are depression, disease burden, increased or decreased body mass index, lower extremity functional limitation, low frequency of social contacts, low level of physical activity, no alcohol use compared to moderate use, poor self-perceived health, smoking, and vision impairments (Stuck, Walthert, Nikolaus, Bula, Hohmann, & Beck, 1999).

Just as dementia can be the result of a variety of different medical conditions, reduced functional ability can also result from a variety of medical problems (e.g., hip fractures, amputations, neurological conditions). Clinicians, therefore, need to assess a broad scope of possible diagnostic factors that can contribute to a decline in functional status and to what degree these are affecting the person's ability to perform ADLs and IADLs.

Another factor to consider is the effect of medications on higher order functioning. Older adults are more sensitive to the direct effects and side effects of medications due to slower metabolisms and are at greater risk of drug interactions due to often being prescribed multiple medications.

Cognitive Underpinnings

Living independently does not require that an individual be cognitively intact, but if cognitive deficits are present, it does require a determination as to what extent they will affect the person's ability to live alone and what, if any, adjustments should be considered to the individual's environment to enhance cognitive strengths. Cognitive factors that can trigger an evaluation of capacity for living independently include, but are not limited to: language deficits, memory deficits, impulsivity, and poor insight.

In order to understand the day-to-day requirements of living alone an individual would need to demonstrate the ability to attend to what needs to be done (i.e., be alert enough to know that things need to be done and to actively plan to do them). Further, an individual would need to know where he or she is, what he or she is doing, and what is the essential purpose of the task at hand. Episodic memory will be helpful to assist the person in recalling when events occurred and which ones did not. Informational memory will help the person understand what items are within the home, what needs to be replaced, and what precautions need to be taken.

Cognitive deficits could also affect a person's ability to apply knowledge and use good judgment. For instance, deficits in executive functioning could lead to impulsivity, disinhibition, decreased initiation, or poor planning that could lead to a person putting him or her self in danger. Language deficits could affect a person's ability to read labels on food and medications, to communicate with others, or to understand what others say. In addition to limiting the person's ability to effectively interpret language-related elements in their environment, it could make it challenging for an adult to direct another person to perform tasks or assist with their personal care. Visuospatial and memory deficits could affect a person's ability to manage medications (Richardson et al., 1995), while visuospatial problem solving and memory have been found to affect money management skills, as well as overall safety (Richardson et al., 1995). Attention deficits have been correlated with balance, falls, and ADL function (Hyndman & Ashburn, 2003).

Clinicians should be aware that an assessment that focuses only on cognitive abilities may not be sufficient to predict functioning and capacity to live independently. A literature review conducted by Royall et al. (2007) found that, although executive function measures were strongly related to higher order

cognitive capacities (e.g., medical and financial decision-making), and that screening measures, such as the Mattis Dementia Rating Scale and Mini-Mental State Exam, were strongly related to disability and functional status, cognition was found to be weakly-to-moderately associated to variations in functional status. These findings suggest that assessment for independent living capacity should incorporate both cognitive and functional assessments in order to get a more accurate understanding of the person's impaired activities.

Psychiatric and Emotional Factors

Severe depression can strongly limit a person's motivation for self-care, and by extension, care of the home. Anxiety is not often a cause of difficulty for independent living, although significant anxiety symptoms may impact the person's abilities to accept help, or to leave the home when necessary to obtain required goods or services that promote the care of the home or person. Hoarding may be associated with obsessive compulsive features and can cause difficulty with independent living.

Symptoms of psychotic disorder are often associated with difficulties with independent living. For instance, negative symptoms have been linked to competence in performing ADLs and ratings of mental health (Meeks & Walker, 1990). Obviously, self-neglect is a negative symptom of schizophrenia and, therefore, impacts the individual's ability to provide for the care of his or her person. Like severe anxiety or PTSD, paranoia could cause a person to be uncomfortable with or to reject help. Hallucinations may make it difficult for the person to accurately assess and resolve problems in their day to day living situation. Substance-use disorders may be associated with inadequate care of oneself or one's home.

Values

The evaluation of the capacity to live independently is laden with values issues. Often individuals have strongly held values related to remaining independent. Further, society's value on living independently can cloud not just the older adult's judgment but that of the clinician who may impose his or her value system on the adult. It is also essential that the clinician be aware of the ethnocentric views that they are bringing to the assessment. For instance, in assessing an adult from a collectivistic-minded society (e.g., Asian or Latino) a clinician will need to take into consideration that the person may not be accustomed to being totally self-reliant and that immediate and extended family may have previously provided a great deal of support. The value of living independently may differ for this person from that of someone who has always had the expectation of being completely self-sufficient and is not accustomed to needing assistance from others.

It will be important to become familiar with a person's culture, religion, and belief system to accurately assess if the older adult's behaviors and judgments are consistent with longstanding practices. For instance, does the individual have the expectation that family will perform certain tasks and therefore lack the initiative or fail to consider the task as something that he or she needs to do for themselves? For example, in certain cultures women are responsible for the home but not for making decisions or financial transactions. In this case, a clinical judgment concerning a woman's financial abilities from this culture could be misinformed because she would not anticipate needing to pay bills or perform other tasks outside of her general responsibilities.

Risks

When weighing the functional data for independent living, the clinician will consider not only the person's values, but the risks. These include estimating the risk to the individual should she or he remain living independently and without a guardian (should the case be considered for guardianship) and the benefits to the person of a supervised living situation. In addition, the risk of imposing a restrictive supervised environment on an older adult which results in the loss of the enjoyment and autonomy must be weighed. Obviously, the most useful source of data for considering these risks is the history of highly undesirable outcomes for the person because of his or her difficulty with self care. When weighing the risks, it is important to consider the seriousness of the risk, the likelihood of the risk, and whether any and all supports that will enhance this individual's capacity to remain independent have been tried.

Steps to Enhance Capacity

There is a huge array of social, medical, and legal interventions that may assist a person in living independently. These are described in Appendix F, and will vary to some extent according to the local Area Agency on Aging, the individual's Medicare or other insurance coverage, and the state elder care framework. The level of assistance that a person requires will depend on various factors, such as cognitive deficits, physical deficits, and medical problems. For instance if someone is mildly physically impaired and the primary deficit is memory, various technological tools may be used to compensate for the memory problems (e.g., using a pager to remind to take medications, to remind about appointments, etc.). Memory books can also be incorporated if the person can be trained to remember to use them. Individuals can also benefit from notes with instructions or reminders posted strategically around the home (e.g., on medicine cabinet, near front door, on refrigerator). If family or friends or other community agencies are available to check in on the adult throughout the day, they can also help to enhance the adult's ability to continue to live independently by taking care of the things that the adult cannot do physically or checking in to ensure that they have performed daily activities and responsibilities. If no family or friends are available to assist the adult in their current home, home health aid, chore services, Meals on Wheels, and other home services may be available. A move to an assisted living and/or transitional living centers may provide the person the opportunity to remain largely independent.

Collaboration with speech therapists and/or cognitive rehabilitation specialists, as well as occupational therapists and physical therapists for adults with cognitive decline and/or physical impairments, can be crucial in assisting them to identify areas of potential improvement.

Clinical Judgment of Capacity for Living Independently

Once the evaluation is completed the clinician will need to integrate the data and come to a clinical decision about the adult's capacity for living independently. It is important for the clinician to consider the adult's culture and support system. Premorbid lifestyle choices should also be considered. For instance, in the case of an individual who was living in shelters or on the street prior to hospitalization and would like to continue to do so, it may be difficult for the clinician (as well as family or other staff) to accept this as an acceptable way to live. For some individuals, however, it is preferable to be homeless and free on the streets than to be in a nursing home where there are rules to follow. This judgment, however, has to be considered in view of any changes in the individual's level of vulnerability and therefore potential risk. A person may have previously been homeless, but this may no longer be feasible, despite longstanding values, if the person has suffered a medical incident (e.g., stroke, amputation) that greatly changes functional abilities. The threshold for capacity to live independently will vary if the person is to live in his or her home or in a shelter; if there are family or friends that can check in on the person or not; if there is only one medication once a day versus multiple medications for life-threatening conditions. The clinical judgment of capacity for living independently is exceedingly difficult. It must integrate all of the assessment data and come to a determination that balances a respect for the individual's autonomy and cultural values, as well as consider the legal standards and social requirements that safeguard not just the individual but communities, as an unsafe individual could potentially cause harm not just to him or herself, but to others and their property.

Clinical Approaches to Assessing Capacity for Living Independently

Clinical approaches to assessing such a broad capacity will likely utilize a wide array of traditional cognitive measures, as well as behavioral, psychiatric, and functional measures. Incorporating both subjective (i.e., what adult self-reports he or she can do) and objective (i.e., performance-based or direct observation) assessments of functional abilities is recommended because they can significantly vary from each other (Glass, 1998). An example of an approach and battery that incorporates the above dimensions follows: a review of medical records, clinical interview, Neurobehavioral Cognitive Status Examination (NCSE) (a.k.a., Cognistat), Repeatable Battery for the Assessment of Neuropsychological Status (RBANS), Wechsler Memory Scale—third edition (WMS-III), Wechsler Abbreviated Scale of Intelligence (WASI), Independent Living Scale (ILS), observation/data collection of in vivo decision-making activities, Geriatric Depression Scale (GDS), and review of medical/pharmacological evaluation to determine if cognitive factors (e.g., confusion) are reversible. Assessment of substance use and misuse of prescription medications can be conducted in order to determine if these are present and potentially affect judgment. This is not an exhaustive list, but rather a list of potential measures that might be incorporated into the evaluation of an older person's capacity to live independently.

Review of Medical Records

Whenever possible, a review of medical records should be considered as it can provide the clinician with a plethora of information about the adult's medical diagnosis and treatments, as well as behaviors. A review of outpatient medical records, for instance, may reveal either consistency in attending appointments or missing many appointments. It can reveal information about the adult's medical progress and compliance (or poor compliance) with treatments and medications. Most importantly it can be used to get an accurate detail of the person's medical diagnosis and medication regimen. Records may also show if the patient was previously referred to, or seen by, mental health services. If the patient has received mental health services, reviewing those records will also be beneficial. The clinician can then use this information to corroborate information given by the adult, as well as to determine if medical or psychological conditions or medications and their side-effects could affect cognition, judgment, and/or physical abilities that would affect the ability to live independently.

The Clinical Interview

The clinical interview will help to establish rapport, as well as to provide the clinician with data regarding the adult's premorbid lifestyle choices, cultural values, and awareness of current medical and physical circumstances that could affect the ability to care for him or herself and live independently. The clinical interview can also provide information on how the adult anticipates he or she will resolve problems. Although the clinical interview can provide crucial information, its interpretation can be subjective, so objective data collection to support the clinical interpretation is recommended.

Some questions to add to a clinical interview that specifically focus on issues relevant to the capacity to live independently are:

1. Where are you living now? How long have you been there?
2. Does anyone live there with you? If not, do you have any fears or concerns about living alone?
3. Does anyone visit on a regular basis?
4. What family and/or friends live in your community who are important to you?
5. What is most important to you about where you live? What makes it "home"?
6. What kind of personal activities do you enjoy doing at home?
7. Are there community activities in which you enjoy participating?
8. What do you like about your house/apartment?
9. What do you not like about your house/apartment? What does not work well for you and why?
10. Do you feel that you can manage the house/apartment on your own? Have you noticed any changes in your abilities to manage?
11. Are there areas of your life that you feel you may need some assistance managing? For instance, do you have any trouble with housekeeping, yard work, preparing meals, shopping, driving, using the telephone, the mail, your health, taking medications, managing your money, or paying bills on your own?
12. Is there someone helping you with any of these things? If so, how long have they been assisting you?
13. If you needed help, who would you like to help you? Is there anyone that you would be wary of? Why?
14. Have you had any safety concerns at home? For instance, have you ever accidentally left the stove or oven on, fallen and been unable to get up by yourself, left your doors unlocked, or invited a stranger into your home?
15. Where would you like to live in the future?
16. Have you ever considered moving to a place where there would be more help for you, such as senior housing, assisted living, or a nursing home? How do you feel about that? What fears or concerns do you have?

Functional Assessment

Functional evaluation includes observation and direct assessment of the adult in day-to-day activities, as well as administration of functional assessment instruments. For instance, for an adult that is hospitalized, feedback from nurses who work with him or her daily can provide information about how the person is functioning within the hospital. Is he forgetting to use a walker? Is she impulsively getting out of bed and falling? Is he wandering outside the room? For an individual who lives in the community, feedback from neighbors, family, and friends can be helpful in getting a broader picture of the individual. For example, they can indicate if they've noticed changes in behaviors, increased need for assistance, or changes in memory? They can corroborate information provided by the adult. A functional assessment is important for an individual that will be living alone because although an adult may know what needs to be done (e.g., take medicine daily), he or she may lack the ability to actually perform the behavior or direct care due to underappreciated cognitive or physical difficulties.

Functional Assessment Instruments

One useful measure of functional ability is the "Independent Living Scales" (ILS). This instrument evaluates an individual's memory and orientation, knowledge about how to manage money, manage home and transportation, knowledge about health and safety, and social adjustment. For instance, in the memory section it asks respondents to remember an appointment, while in the health and safety section it asks examinees to demonstrate how they would call an ambulance. In the managing money section basic skills, such as the ability to count coins, write checks, and read a bill, are assessed. In the home and transportation sections the adult is asked to find information in a phone book, to write a check, and to discuss precautions a person can take while bathing. Responses are given 0, 1, or 2 points and totaled within each subtest to create a profile. The scores can fall within one of three areas: dependent, moderately independent, and independent. This measure helps the clinician identify areas in which the adult may require assistance.

Additional functional instruments are described in Appendix B.

Cognitive Assessment

Objective testing to determine cognitive abilities and how these may affect decision making and the ability to live independently can be completed with brief assessment instruments such as the NCSE or RBANS. The NCSE allows a clinician to assess orientation, attention/concentration, language abilities, construction abilities, memory, abstract reasoning, and judgment. The NCSE has separate norms for individuals over age 65 and is available in various languages. The RBANS assesses for learning and memory for both immediate visual and verbal information, attention, language, visuospatial abilities, and delayed memory. The RBANS has norms for ages 20-89. These brief assessment instruments can administered in 15 to 45 minutes and additional measures, such as instruments to assess executive function, can be included with these tools to make the assessment more comprehensive.

A more extensive neuropsychological battery may include a WMS-III, the WASI, and additional measures of executive functioning. The combination of these measures can provide a clinician with an idea of baseline abilities, areas of cognitive deficits, and areas of cognitive strength. Together with functional assessment these tools provide insight into how cognition may impact a person's ability to perform the day-to-day tasks required for living independently. These are described in Appendix C.

Psychiatric and Emotional Assessment

Measures to assess mood disorders can be incorporated into the evaluation to determine how much they may be contributing to behavior and decision making. Examples include the Beck Depression Inventory, Beck Anxiety Inventory, and Geriatric Depression Scale. These are described in Appendix D.

Case Example

Introduction to Psychological Evaluation for Independent Living Capacity

Mr. Cruz is a 63-year-old never-married monolingual English speaking Latino male who suffered a left occipital-parietal stroke with subsequent right-sided upper and lower extremity weakness, memory deficits, as well as visuospatial and language deficits. Premorbid medical history included prior occipital and cerebellar infarcts, mild diffuse atrophy with periventricular white matter changes, a diagnosis of dementia, hypertension, hypercholesterolemia, and polycysthemia secondary to tobacco use.

A routine psychological evaluation was done with the patient at time of admission. On admission he presented with severe expressive aphasia, and deficits in visual spatial processing, reading, writing, attention, and memory. He made significant improvements in various cognitive and physical areas so his attending physician referred him for a psychological evaluation to determine capacity to live independently after inpatient rehabilitation therapy was completed.

Informed Consent

Mr. Cruz was informed that the purpose of the evaluation was to gather information about his capacity to live independently. The benefits and risks of the evaluation were discussed with him, specifically that we would get a better understanding of his functional status and it would help the team with discharge planning, but that it might show that he cannot live independently and would need to reside in a supervised living situation. He was further advised that if the findings indicated he did not have capacity to live independently, the results of the evaluation could possibly be used to support a guardianship petition.

It is important to discuss the purpose, as well as risks and benefits of an independent living capacity evaluation in order to get informed consent, but also because the results can be life altering. It is also a way to show respect, empower the patient, and engage them in the process. Clinically, advising patients that their capacity is being questioned often results in less resistance to testing and generally leads to a good therapeutic alliance that is based on trust. Mr. Cruz agreed to participate in the evaluation.

Social History

Mr. Cruz was born in the Midwest and moved to the West Coast during his twenties. He completed high school and worked in the fitness industry. His career had focused on weight lifting and working as a trainer.

Premorbid history of mental health problems was denied. He reported smoking one-and-a-half packs of cigarettes per day for 48 years and remote history of steroid use. No other substance use history was indicated.

Evaluation Procedure

Clinical Interview, Cognistat, ILS Managing Home and Health and Safety subtests, and portions of Guide to Capacity Questionnaire. He was observed in physical therapy, occupational therapy, and speech therapy over a two-week period to assess functional abilities.

Behavioral Observations

Mr. Cruz was awake, alert, and fully oriented. His demeanor towards the evaluation was cooperative and forthcoming with mild underlying resistance. He was noted to make general statements about his abilities and then self correct. For instance, he stated he could walk as well as anyone in the hospital and then self-corrected stating that was probably an exaggeration, as he still needed to improve his ambulation abilities. Right-sided weakness was significantly improved from time of admission but coordination deficits were still present. He was noted to use his right hand for writing and pointing at items throughout the evaluation. Psychotic thought process was not present. Emotionally, patient shared that he was nervous as he knew he was being evaluated. Affect was full range and mood was euthymic with mild underlying anxiety. It was noted that patient reported being thirsty and dizzy and was concerned about being hypoglycemic.

Cognistat

Mr. Cruz' performance was in the average range for orientation, attention, language abilities, calculations, and reasoning abilities. It was noted that impulsivity led to errors but he was able to self correct. For instance, he said it was September 1995 and when asked if that was correct he immediately stated it was wrong. Language comprehension, repetition, and naming were within normal limits. Mr. Cruz was also able to describe a picture of a boy fishing. He was able to do simple calculations of addition, division, and subtraction. Abstract thought process was within normal limits and significantly improved from time of admission. Judgment was also within normal limits. His performance for visuoconstructional tasks and memory tasks was severely impaired. He was unable to replicate various block constructions or copy a geometric design. He was able to learn four words but after a brief delay required multiple choice, cuing to remember three words and was unable to identify the fourth word. Overall executive functioning was impaired. On Trails 1 his performance was slow but accurate (10th percentile). However, he was unable to complete Trails B, which requires him to switch between two patterns. This task was discontinued at three minutes. Mr. Cruz repeated the same error: an inability to switch between the patterns, despite numerous repetitions of task demands. These results suggest that Mr. Cruz will have difficulty when trying to complete two tasks at the same time, especially as task complexity increases.

Independent Living Scales

On the Managing Home and Transportation subtest Mr. Cruz was unable to do four items due to visuospatial deficits. He got 16 out of 22 possible points (73%). In general, he was able to discuss accurate ways of managing public transportation and getting information via telephone, as well as appropriate times to contact his landlord. On the Health and Safety subtest he attained a standard score of 42, placing him in the moderately dependent range. He was able to discuss reasonable actions to take in various emergency situations related to signs of a heart attack, taking care of body, unintentional weight loss, bleeding, and loss of hearing and vision. He had difficulty comprehending several questions and therefore gave fair to poor responses. For instance, when asked what he would do if he couldn't hear most conversations he replied, "I guess I wasn't meant to hear it." When it was re-worded as, "What if you had hearing loss?" he replied, "Get hearing checked. It could be dangerous ...." He lost points for responses that were impulsive and was noted to self-correct his impulsivity on at least one question by stating, "that would be an extreme response."

Clinical Interview

Mr. Cruz began the evaluation by discussing his understanding of discharge recommendations, rehabilitation progress, and medical problems. He shared that we were in a rehabilitation hospital for people who had "seizures . . . aneurysms." He was able to state that he had problems with memory, ambulation, and vision secondary to an "aneurysm." Mr. Cruz was able to discuss his visual field cut. He was not able to name his medications, but was able to reliably state what they were not for (e.g., seizures, pain, and diabetes). He was unsure if he was taking a blood thinner, but affirmed that he was taking medicine to control his blood pressure.

In discussing his discharge plans, patient shared that he wanted to go home and live independently and that he understood that he needed help with his medications. Upon further query, patient was able to discuss other possible complications he could experience due to his current deficits. For instance, Mr. Cruz agreed that he would not be able to pay bills due to his visual problems and difficulties with writing. He agreed that he could have problems shopping and cooking as well, due to his visual deficits.

Therapy Observations

Mr. Cruz was observed in therapies over a two-week period. Level of agitation observed at time of admission had decreased as his abilities improved. He was noted to follow directions, participate, and cooperate with limits set by therapists. His recall for events that occurred in therapies was variable, as was his recall for environmental information. For instance, on one occasion he was found sitting next to another patient's bed and erroneously saying it was his bed; he was actually assigned to a bed on the other side of the room. Therapists noted that his memory deficits, as well as premorbid personality style, limited carry-over for strategies taught. At time of discharge he was able to ambulate independently but could still not navigate around the unit or from the unit to the therapy gyms without getting lost.

Impressions and Recommendations

Mr. Cruz is a 63-year-old single male who is status post left occipital-parietal ischemic stroke with subsequent right-sided weakness, visuospatial deficits, graphomotor deficits, and memory problems. His history is negative for mental health problems and suggestive of a determined, independent individual. Premorbid personality and lifestyle are likely to lead to attempt to present in better light and to overstate his abilities, however, upon query he is likely to correct himself.

Attention, language, and reasoning abilities improved since admission two weeks prior, however, he continues to present with deficits in vision and memory. Mr. Cruz expresses awareness of memory deficits, as well as his right visual field cut. His insight into his own medical condition seems fair to good as indicated by his ability to discuss his various medical treatments. His awareness of his memory problems, however, appears to cause increased anxiety that leads him to second guess some of his responses and seek reassurance from others.

He expressed understanding of potential dangers of returning to live alone and based on his functional abilities he would be a significant danger to himself if he were to return to live independently. Mr. Cruz agrees and is agreeable to being discharged to a nursing facility while he continues to recover from his stroke and to re-assess his ability to live independently in the future.

Although financial capacity was not a focus of this evaluation, his visual deficits will most likely interfere with his ability to manage his finances. It is suggested social work assist the patient to identify an individual that can assist him with finances or explore other options.

In conclusion, at this time, Mr. Cruz has capacity to make and communicate decisions, and limited ability to implement decisions made. He has capacity to understand the risks and consequences of his behavior. His ability to complete ADLs, to manage himself or his property, to protect himself, and perform or obtain services, however, is limited. He is likely to be dependent on others to a great degree and requires care and treatment for his own welfare. Mr. Cruz overall does not have capacity to live independently at this time due to functional deficits related to cognition, sensory deficits, and memory deficits that could result in him putting himself or others at risk for harm.

VII. Undue Influence

To this point, the handbook has focused on a conceptual framework and assessment tools for understanding decisional capacity. Psychologists working with older adults may come across a related but distinct area of law, that of undue influence. In Chapter 2, relevant legal definitions are given to describe undue influence. The goal of the current chapter is to review critical elements of the legal definitions, further describe the dynamic of undue influence, introduce clinical frameworks for thinking about undue influence, provide suggestions for assessment, and give a clinical case example. It should be noted that little empirical research exists to guide clinicians in their assessment of undue influence. At present a number of theoretical frameworks are used to understand undue influence and to present the data in court. We will begin by briefly reviewing relevant legal definitions.

Legal Standards of Undue Influence

The *Restatement of Contracts*, an authoritative secondary legal source, defines undue influence as follows:

> Undue influence is unfair persuasion of a party who is under the domination of the person exercising the persuasion or who by virtue of the relation between them is justified in assuming that that person will not act in a manner inconsistent with his welfare ("Restatement (Second) of Contracts," 1981).

The doctrine is akin to doctrines of fraud and duress and may be alleged in legal transactions, such as executing a will, entering a contract, or conveying property to another, as well as cases of financial abuse, sexual abuse, and even homicide. Other definitions stress the psychological component of undue influence, the intentional and improper use of power or trust in a way that deprives a person of free will and substitutes another's objective.

Consent to a contract, transaction, or relationship, or to conduct, is voidable if the consent is obtained through undue influence (Black's Law Dictionary, 2004). While diminished capacity may make one more vulnerable to undue influence, it is not a necessary component of the dynamic. Therefore, undue influence can be present even when the victim clearly possesses mental capacity. Much of the law of undue influence is forged in state-specific case law that exhibits a great deal of variability in defining undue influence, so the law of each state must be consulted.

Evaluations to examine the potential presence of undue influence require knowledge of several concepts:

Capacity: Broadly refers to an individual s ability to receive and evaluate information and make and express a decision.

Financial Exploitation: A type of elder abuse, involving the improper use or theft of another s assets.

Undue Influence: When exploiters, whether family, acquaintances, or strangers, use their power to *deceptively* gain control over the decision making of a victim. Often involves financial exploitation.

Undue Influence in Relationships Based on Trust and Confidence

Keeping in mind the wide variability across states, courts often require two elements to be proven in a case of undue influence involving a contract: (1) a special relationship between the parties based on confidence and trust; and (2) intentional and improper influence or persuasion of the weaker party by the stronger.

Psychologists performing assessments of undue influence must therefore determine if a confidential relationship exists that would provide the opportunity for undue influence to occur. More descriptively, undue influence occurs when a person uses his or her role and power to exploit the trust, dependency, and fear of another. Perpetrators of undue influence use this power to deceptively gain control over the decision making of the second person (Singer, 1993). Psychologists working with the older adults on cases regarding financial capacity need to be knowledgeable about undue influence and integrate that knowledge into every stage of the assessment process.

Psychological Frameworks for Understanding Undue Influence

Undue influence is an emerging area of study for psychologists and, to date, there is little published research to draw upon. Here we introduce several models, but draw upon common elements in our discussion. We present four models that have been used to understand undue influence in older adults. Margaret Singer, PhD, an early noted expert in this field originally developed her model regarding undue influence out of her work with cult victims. Subsequent clinical models, such as the Brandle/ Heisler/ Steigel Model, Blum's "IDEAL" model, and Bernatz's "SCAM" model draw heavily on the work of Singer and her collaborator, Abraham Nievod, PhD, JD.

Singer's framework emphasized social influence conditions that the suspect crafts unknowingly to the victim. These conditions included creating isolation, fostering a siege mentality, inducing dependency, promoting a sense of powerlessness, manipulating fears and vulnerabilities, and keeping the victim unaware and uninformed.

Undue Influence **IDEAL** Protocol

Isolation
Dependency
Emotional manipulation and/or
  Exploitation of a vulnerability
Acquiescence; and
Loss

Bennett Blum, MD, a psychiatrist, expanded on Singer's model to create a model to understand undue influence emphasizing the social conditions prevalent in cases of undue influence situations. Dr. Blum's "IDEAL" model is organized around five main categorical headings and several subdivisions. These headings include isolation from family and friends; dependency on the perpetrator; emotional manipulation of the victim; acquiescence of the victim due to the previous factors; and financial loss. Dr. Blum created a practical and qualitative tool, the "Undue Influence Worksheet," used by some lawyers, court investigators, law enforcement personnel and adult protective services workers. The Blum Worksheet is essentially a data collection tool, organized around the five main categorical headings and several subdivisions. Its aim is to help clarify for the user whether excessive manipulation is present. The data then must be evaluated in light of local statutes and case law defining undue influence.

A third clinical framework has been developed by clinical and forensic psychologist Susan I. Bernatz, PhD. The "SCAM" model builds on Singer's and Blum's work in which social influence conditions are emphasized, yet also includes factors that contribute to the victim's "susceptibility" and addresses the perpetrators "active procurement" of the legal or financial transaction(s). The "SCAM" model views undue influence as an inter-relational concept between the victim and the perpetrator and incorporates four main categories that include: susceptibility factors of the victim; a confidential and trusting relationship between the victim and perpetrator; active procurement of the legal and financial transactions by the perpetrator; and, monetary loss of the victim. There are additional subcategories for susceptibility and confidential relationship. Additional factors that fall under the susceptibility category include: medical and psychological factors that contribute to impaired cognition and lack of capacity of the victim; dependency on the perpetrator, which is often a by-product of impaired functional ability and capacity of the victim; isolation of the victim, which includes physical or emotional isolation; and, the victim's knowledge and previous habits.

Undue Influence **SCAM** Model
Susceptibility
Confidential Relationship
Active Procurement
Monetary Loss

Undue influence is a type of elder abuse. Older women who are White and live alone are often considered to be the most likely victims of financial elder abuse that is reported (National Center for Elder Abuse, 1998). A widely-cited profile of a target for financial abuse is generally a White woman over 75 years of age who is living alone (Rush & Lank, 2000; Tueth, 2000). Additionally, the victim's ability to resist undue influence has been noted to be lessened when the person or victim is dependent on the caretaker or influencer. Spar et al., (1992) noted that any debilitating mental or physical illness resulting in dependence on caretakers will increase susceptibility to undue influence. Dependency can include physical dependence, such as food preparation, assistance with medications, helping with bill paying, checkbook management, reading bank statements, or taking the victim to the physician's office. Emotional dependence can include emotional support and encouragement, and information dependence can include dependence on information, such as financial or legal advice.

In the SCAM model the vulnerable or susceptible individual also develops a confidential and trusting relationship with the perpetrator. The victim's trust is gained through various tactics of persuasion, manipulation, and deception. Some of these tactics come in the form of social influence techniques, such as liking and reciprocity (Regan et al., 1971), and authority (Milgram, 1963), and at other times the strategy may be to just keep the victim unaware and uninformed about the legal or financial transactions. These weapons of influence are utilized by the perpetrator to heighten the victim's reliance and dependence on the perpetrator. For example, a common method of

persuasion that a suspect may exploit is that of reciprocity. The suspect may perform caretaking duties for the victim, such as driving to doctors' appointments, filling prescriptions, or cooking meals. The victim often feels that he or she "owes" the perpetrator something. The victim is, thus, often taken advantage of by the person who gains from the victim's indebtedness. Influence becomes "undue" when the perpetrator exploits the victim's dependency and trust for personal financial gain. It is this trust and dependency that gives the perpetrator the ability to steal the victim's assets.

There are many potential "indicators" of undue influence to bear in mind. These factors include both demographics that increase risk and behavior changes such as: White women over the age of 75 years of age, recently widowed men and women, individuals who are geographically isolated, and individuals who have had a significant or unexplained emotional change, such as a marked depression and or insidious memory loss or other cognitive deficits. In terms of behavioral changes, a comparison of the victim's past spending habits with current habits is critical to assess. For example, the victim that has lived modestly throughout life but now begins to make large purchases and/or give large amounts of money and gifts to a new "best friend" may be a victim of undue influence. Financial transactions that are uncharacteristic of the victim may be another marker of undue influence. For example, bank records indicating many ATM transactions that are not possible for a homebound older adult could be suspect, as would be an older adult allegedly performing on-line bank transactions but who does not own a computer. The purpose of these transactions may be to transfer funds into "joint-accounts" that the victim and suspect are both signors on, but is controlled by the alleged influencer. Additional indicators may include changes in the victim's will or trust that are not consistent with a previous disposition, and the absence of any third party advisers. Upon questioning the victim it is often determined that the suspect has been initiating all of the aspects of the financial and or legal transactions, including providing transportation

Summary of Undue Influence Models			
Singer/Nievod Model	Blum IDEAL Model	Bernatz SCAM Model	Brandle/Heisler/Stiegel Model
Factors: 1. Isolation 2. Dependency 3. Creating Siege Mentality 4. Sense of Powerlessness 5. Sense of Fear/Vulnerability 6. Staying Unaware	*Factors:* 1. **I**solation 2. **D**ependency 3. **E**motional manipulation and/or **E**xploitation of a vulnerability 4. **A**cquiescence 5. **L**oss	*Elements:* 1. **S**usceptibility 2. **C**onfidential Relationship 3. **A**ctive Procurement 4. **M**onetary Loss	*Goal:* • Financial Exploitation *Typical Perpetrator Tactics:* 1. Isolate from others and information 2. Create fear 3. Prey on vulnerabilities 4. Create dependency 5. Create lack of faith in own abilities 6. Induce shame and secrecy 7. Perform intermittent acts of kindness 8. Keep unaware

to the bank, hiring a notary or an attorney, printing out forms, etc. This type of active

procurement can be used as evidence of undue influence.

The Brandle/Heisler/Stiegel model describes perpetrator behavior in cases of undue influence. Although psychologists will primarily be asked to assess older victims, knowledge regarding the alleged influencer can be useful in determining the potential presence of undue influence. The influencer is often in the home close to the victim and may even be interviewed by the psychologist as a collateral source.

In the Brandle/Heisler/Stiegel model, the influencer is described as a predator who targets isolated elders, often in places such as supermarkets and drug stores, and "grooms" the person through an initial show of friendship and caring. Once trust has been established, the influencer will use a variety of tactics to increase their power and control and diminish the control of the older adults, including isolation, fear, shame, with intermittent acts of kindness. At the same time, the alleged influencer will work to keep the victim unaware of their intent and the loss of assets.

Summary of Clinical Models

In Chapter 2, we provide a summary of potential risk factors identified by the courts in cases of undue influence, including opportunity, motive, unnaturalness of transaction, susceptibility, and the use of unnatural devices. In this chapter, we have emphasized clinical factors that psychologists can assess and potentially describe in a report provided to the courts as evidence. The frameworks presented differ in their specifics, but there are some important common elements to keep in mind while conducting an assessment. These include factors that increase susceptibility of the victim, the presence of a confidential relationship, a mechanism for fraud to occur, and monetary transfers that benefit the alleged influencer.

Writing About Undue Influence in Your Report

Undue influence evaluations include all of the information that goes into a capacity assessment (purpose of evaluation, history of problem, medical, social, occupational history, neuropsychological testing, discussion of results, and financial capacity findings), as well as a discussion of the factors that have contributed to the older adult's susceptibility to undue influence. Copious records are gathered in these cases to develop a timeline of events and to factually support the expert's opinion. These records may include medical, law enforcement, legal and financial, deposition testimony, estate planning documents, interviews with the victim, and collateral informants.

Case Example

Ms. Johnson is an 86-year-old female referred for a neuropsychological evaluation to determine her decisional capacity to make financial decisions for herself and to determine relevant factors that may have contributed to Ms. Johnson's susceptibility to undue influence and inability to resist fraud in the time frame in question.

Presenting Problem

Ms. Johnson is an 86-year-old widowed female currently residing in her home. She owns her home and given its proximity to the ocean, it is worth over $2 million. The case was initially brought to APS due to a potential case of physical and financial elder abuse. The primary referral questions were to assess Ms. Johnson's ability to complete financial transactions and to assess whether or not she was susceptible to undue influence. The APS report documented the following concerns: the victim had made recent changes to her will and trust. However, she had carried a diagnosis of dementia since early 2003. Furthermore, APS reported that Ms. Johnson prepared a cassette tape that discussed her final wishes—to have an autopsy of her body and an accounting of her estate upon her passing. Her housekeeper was the reporter in this case and handed over the tape to law enforcement.

This request for autopsy was in direct opposition to her previous wishes as set forth in a Durable Power of Attorney over Health Care written in 2003. Further, she had voiced to friends that she thought the alleged influencer was "trying to kill her." At the same time, the victim seemed powerless to escape from the confidential relationship, as she had become completely dependent upon suspect. Interviews with neighbors indicated that the alleged influencer had moved in with the victim shortly after the loss of her husband and provided welcomed companionship. The victim and alleged influencer appeared to have met at a church that they both have belonged to for years. At first the two were seen as close friends, even traveling together on vacation. Over time, the relationship became increasingly exploitive. Financial records indicated that the victim had paid for the alleged influencer's living expenses for the past five years and had given her $800,000 in payments by check and account transfers. In summary, the victim was at risk for financial and physical harm. Based on the above information a medical workup and neuropsychological evaluation were conducted.

Informed Consent

Ms. Johnson was explained the purpose of the evaluation and that the results may be used by this examiner in court in prosecution and litigation involving financial decision making and undue influence. She appeared to understand the purpose, risk, and benefits of the assessment and consented to the evaluation.

Social History

Ms. Johnson reported that she was raised in a local community, in a close family with several siblings who are all now deceased. She reported that she attended high school and junior college without difficulty. She was married to her husband for over forty years although had no children from this union. She enjoyed working as an office manager for a local company for over 25 years, but then retired and enjoyed traveling with her husband.

Medical History

Ms. Johnson carries a history of multiple cancers, and is post p surgery and chemotherapy in 2002. Additionally, she has a history of hyperlipidemia, hypertension, macular degeneration and depression (1993-2005).

Current Medications

Restoril	7.5 1 qhs prn

| Actonel | 35 1 TAB |
| Clonidine | HCL .1 mg. qd |

Neuroimaging was performed in 2003 and the CT findings revealed an old lacunar infarct in the left cerebellar hemisphere and mild microvascular ischemia in the left frontal lobe. Additionally, Ms. Johnson was seen by a neurologist in July of 2003 where her performance on the MMSE was 24/30. At this time she was placed on Aricept, although she stopped taking the medication. Ms. Johnson did not have any follow-up visits with the neurologist. Ms. Johnson is completely dependent on the alleged influencer, who has hired caregivers to take care of her in her home. Ms. Johnson needs assistance with dressing, showering, meal preparation and clean up, home maintenance, bill paying, transportation, and medical advocacy and support.

Clinical Interview

This examiner met with Ms. Johnson in her home. She was casually dressed, well coiffed, and presented with good hygiene. She was pleasant and cooperative and her mood appeared to be slightly blunted and her affect mildly restricted. At times she appeared anxious, asking if the alleged influencer was in the home and checking the time. She displayed consistent motivation throughout the evaluation and results of this testing are judged to be a valid indicator of her current ability.

During the clinical interview Ms. Johnson was a poor historian and unable to provide global or detailed histories with regard to her medical conditions or her finances and estate planning. When asked if she had any previous history of surgeries she remarked, "not that I know of." Ms. Johnson was also deficient in her financial knowledge. She could not recall where she did her banking, what the name of her brokerage institution was, or what was the purpose of a trust. Ms. Johnson did acknowledge that in early 2004 she began to give the suspect an "allowance" of $500 a week in exchange for the suspect's care-giving duties and assistance with managing her finances. She denied ever giving the suspect any financial gifts or loans.

Cognitive Testing

On the Repeatable Battery for the Assessment of Neuropsychological Skills (RBANS) she had the following results:

Ability	Percentile	Range
Attention	58%	Average
Visual-Spatial	< 1%	Severely Impaired
Language	8%	Borderline
Immediate Memory	0.1%	Impaired
Delayed Memory	0.1%	Impaired

Additional executive testing found severe impairment on Trails B, although average ability on the clock drawing task. Functional testing in the area of money management on the Independent Living Scale (ILS) placed her performance in the impaired range or requiring supervision in the area of money management. When asked to name one thing she could do to keep from being cheated out of her money she replied, "I have no idea, I don't know how to stop it."

An assessment of mood using the Geriatric Depression Scale was consistent with the presence of significant depression (18/30). In addition, the client reported symptoms consistent with an anxiety disorder, including feeling fearful, on edge, and reported that she worried all the time about the alleged influencer.

Summary

Ms. Johnson is an 83-year-old female with a history of multiple medical surgeries who is currently living at home with 24-hour, 7-day a week care. Concerns about her current financial decisions and the possibility of her being a victim of elder physical and financial abuse have been raised. Specifically, it is alleged that she may have been the victim of undue influence. Based on clinical interview and cognitive testing, the following conclusions are offered:

Regarding her cognition she has adequate attention, however her short- and long-term verbal memory, executive functioning, and visual spatial abilities are impaired. She was impoverished in her ability to adequately explain her current finances or perform simple and complex financial tasks (write out two checks and reconcile the amount with a balance previously given to her) and to perform a simple two-step operational math problem (if her medical insurance company pays for 20% of her medical bill of $350, what does she owe). She was also unable to describe what the purpose of a trust or will.

Regarding her capacity to make financial decisions it is this clinician's opinion that Ms. Johnson lacks the capacity to make financial decisions given her cognitive dysfunction and probable dementia diagnosis. She has a deficient understanding of the nature and consequences of her financial decisions. Ms. Johnson is unable to manage her checkbook, understand her bank and brokerage account statements, conceptually understands the legal vehicle of a trust or will and is unable to enter into either buy/sell agreements with regards to her stock portfolio or contractual agreements regarding her real estate.

Furthermore, it is also this clinician's opinion that Ms. Johnson has been susceptible to undue influence for several years beginning with the loss of her husband in early 2002. This clinician's opinion is based on a review of medical, law enforcement, legal and financial records; estate planning documents included in this case record; cognitive testing and interview with Ms. Johnson; interview with her caregiver, and with friends of Ms. Johnson's for 15 years; deposition testimony from her caregiver, estate planning attorney, and the alleged perpetrator; and a review of the deposition video of the perpetrator.

There are numerous factors that contributed to Ms. Johnson's susceptibility that include: her psychological and medical conditions, (history of depression 1993-2005), cognitive deficits, dementia syndrome, depression and anxiety, and medical conditions, which included a history of cancer). Further, Ms. Johnson has been dependent on the alleged influencer for all of her IADLS, including medical and financial assistance. The alleged influencer is aware of Ms. Johnson's difficulties but did not provide Ms. Johnson with any third-party advisers to help in the management of her estate or to provide Ms. Johnson with a system of checks and balances. Additionally, Ms. Johnson changed her disposition plan to her will in the time in question to benefit the alleged influencer and these changes were significantly different from Ms. Johnson's previous plans and wishes that appeared to benefit several foundations, and friends, as well as the alleged influencer. The alleged influencer initiated the transactions and was solely responsible for transferring the large amount of assets into an account that she held jointly with Ms. Johnson.

Furthermore, Ms. Johnson instilled her trust and confidence to the alleged influencer. Ms. Johnson was befriended by the victim at a church that they both had belonged to for numerous years. The alleged influencer initially began to assist Ms. Johnson with some of her care-giving needs and much-needed social support after the death of her husband. Due to the victim's infirmities and isolation from others Ms. Johnson became more dependent on the alleged influencer, which eventually led to the suspect paying the victim's bills, reconciling her bank account, and eventually obtaining a Durable Power of Attorney over the victim's finances. Eventually, the alleged influencer also moved in with the victim and opened many new bank accounts with both her and the victim as co-signors. The victim was unaware of the new accounts that had been opened. According to the detective's report and the forensic handwriting analysis, Ms. Johnson did not write any of the checks that were written to the alleged influencer. Unfortunately, Ms. Johnson's trust, dependency, and vulnerabilities appeared to have been exploited for the alleged influencer's financial gain.

Recommendations

1. Financial and physical protection of Ms. Johnson. Based on the results of this evaluation, it is recommended that Ms. Johnson be appointed a temporary conservator to oversee her health care and finances and represent Ms. Johnson until this investigation and litigation is over.
2. Dementia work-up. Results of this evaluation reveal that Ms. Johnson has an

insidious memory decline and cognitive testing consistent with a dementia syndrome. A full medical evaluation for dementia and reversible causes of cognitive impairment are recommended.

3. Ms. Johnson is currently on medications that have the potential to impair cognition. A medication evaluation is recommended.

4. Ms. Johnson evidenced significant depression and anxiety symptoms during the evaluation, and further treatment is recommended. Ms. Johnson may benefit from a thorough mental health work-up, including psychopharmacological and psychosocial interventions.

VIII. Working with Lawyers and Courts

Psychologists engaged in capacity assessment may receive referrals from lawyers for evaluations, and will respond to court orders for clinical evaluation in guardianship proceedings. This chapter will examine key factors in working with lawyers, including consultations, requests for formal assessments, client consent, information needed, and use of the report. Next, the chapter will describe how psychologists can best work with the court in the context of a guardianship proceeding.

Accepting Referrals From a Lawyer

When and Why a Lawyer Might Seek Your Help

Capacity evaluations can be valuable to lawyers and their clients because they furnish objective cognitive and behavioral data and professional expertise. The potential uses of clinical opinion on client capacity include:

- Determination of whether a prospective client has sufficient legal capacity to enter into a lawyer-client relationship;
- Determination of whether a client has capacity to undertake a specific legal transaction;
- Evidence in a guardianship proceeding;
- Expert testimony in a deposition or courtroom hearing;
- Clarification of the areas of diminished capacity, as well as retained strengths;
- Affirmation of the client's capacity;
- Expert opinion on conclusions of other psychological evaluations, including those submitted by opposing counsel;
- Justification of the attorney's concerns about capacity to disbelieving clients and family members;
- Expert advice on strategies to compensate for identified mental deficits;
- Indication of the need for protective action by the attorney; and

- Recommendations concerning any follow-up testing.

How to Connect with Lawyers

Lawyer referrals for capacity consultation or assessment can enhance your practice and sharpen your expertise. Legal rules of ethics on clients with diminished capacity allow the lawyer to find an "appropriate diagnostician," but do not specify who is "appropriate" nor how to identify such a practitioner. Psychologists can help to make the connection—reaching out and developing referral resources so that a lawyer will know where to turn when the need arises.

One starting point is the local Area Agency on Aging for the county, city, or multi-county area of your practice. Under the Older Americans Act, Area Agencies on Aging are responsible for planning and funding a wide range of services for older persons. They typically provide extensive information and referral services, and it would behoove a psychologist whose practice focuses on older people to seek out and meet with the nearest Area Agency on Aging. Such agencies frequently are in close touch with local elder law attorneys. To find your local Area Agency on Aging, contact the Eldercare Locator at 1-800-677-1116, or online at www.eldercare.gov.

State bar associations have sections on aging or disability; a list is available from the ABA Commission on Law and Aging (www.abanet.org/aging/resources/statemap.shtml). Some local bar associations have sections or committees as well. In addition, the National Academy of Elder Law Attorneys has members throughout the country, and a number of state chapters (www.naela.com). In areas without a bar committee on aging or a NAELA chapter, interested psychologists could contact the local probate or mental health section of the bar association. An offer to make a presentation on capacity assessment often will be welcomed by state or local bar groups.

Also, get to know local legal services staff. Some legal services or legal aid programs have a designated attorney or paralegal serving elders. Often these programs are funded through the Area Agencies on Aging with Older Americans Act funds. Finally, each state has a "protection and advocacy agency" designated under federal law to provide legal representation and other advocacy services to people with disabilities. Connections with this state office may be useful, as well (http://www.napas.org/).

Consultation: A lawyer s conversation with a clinician to discuss concerns about the client s presentation. Usually client is not identified and consultation does not require client consent.

Referral: A formal referral to a clinician for evaluation, which may or may not result in a written report. Requires client consent.

Informal Consultation with a Lawyer

It is important to distinguish informal consultations that a lawyer might seek with a psychologist from formal referrals for assessments. Sometimes—instead of or preliminary to seeking a formal assessment—a lawyer may seek an informal private consultation to discuss and clarify specific capacity issues before proceeding further with representation. In such a consultation, the lawyer can discuss client communications and reactions, as well as the legal transaction for which capacity is required. The lawyer can seek

---

Uses of informal consultation

- Clinical interpretation of problem
- Informal clinical opinion on capacity
- Suggestions for enhancing capacity
- Additional questions to ask client

If client is not identified, no consent necessary, and lawyer pays fee.

---

an informal opinion on the question of capacity—and on the question of whether a formal assessment is necessary. The clinician can raise questions the lawyer might have overlooked, allay or reframe the lawyer's concerns, and suggest strategies for enhancing client capacity.

A preliminary up-front consultation on capacity can bring a lot of "bang for the buck"— in some cases saving the lawyer and the client a great deal of time, money, and angst if it avoids an unnecessary formal assessment. Or it may provide reassurance that a formal assessment is indeed the right step, as well as an indication about what kind of assessment might be optimal.

In such an informal consultation, the client may or may not be identified. If the client is identified in the consultation—or if your community is small enough that the lawyer would know who the client is— ethical considerations on client consent come into play, just as they would for a formal assessment (see below). However, if the client is not identified, the question of consent for the assessment does not arise. The consultation is simply professional advice to the lawyer, paid for by the lawyer— simplifying the process greatly.

Referrals for Formal Assessment

An attorney may feel compelled by capacity concerns, litigation strategy, or other case circumstances to seek an independent formal capacity evaluation by a psychologist or other clinician. Such a decision is significant because it necessarily involves disclosure to the client of an attorney's concerns or litigation strategy, and requires a client's consent. It represents a significant step by the attorney that can impact the attorney-client relationship in both positive and negative ways.

Be aware that a formal assessment is not without danger for the lawyer, as there is a risk of potential adverse use of the assessment against the lawyer's client. Though the report may be protected under psychologist-patient privilege and attorney-client privilege when the client refuses to consent to disclosure, these privileges are variable under state law and subject to a host of exceptions and interpretations. Their protection from discovery in civil litigation is not absolute (Powell & Link, 1994; Ludington, 1962). Thus, it should be emphasized that the clinical evaluation *need not result in a formal written report.* The lawyer may instruct the psychologist to conduct the evaluation, and then to call the lawyer with preliminary, unwritten conclusions, after which the lawyer can state whether or not the psychologist should commit the opinion to writing. Thus, it is important for a psychologist to clarify with the lawyer beforehand whether a written report is desired.

Client Consents Needed in Referral From Lawyers

If a lawyer seeks to refer a client to a psychologist for a formal capacity assessment, there are several hurdles of consent. It can be a tricky process, since consent requires some level of capacity, and capacity is at issue.

Lawyers are bound by ethical rules to get the consent of the client for a clinical referral. As a practical matter, there can be no referral unless the client at some level agrees to have an appointment with a clinician and to participate in the interview and the selected assessment tests.

Once the client has made contact with the psychologist or other clinician, the assessor will need to ensure there is sufficient informed consent to conduct the evaluation (see Chapter 4).

Finally, the clinician then must get the client's consent to provide the test results to the lawyer under the privacy requirements of the Health Insurance Portability and Accountability Act (HIPAA, 1996).

What Information Do You Need from the Lawyer?

To be most responsive to the lawyer's request for a capacity assessment, a psychologist or other clinician needs full information. This is best set out in a well-tailored referral letter from the lawyer, which should include at least:

- background information about the client and the circumstances;
- the reason for the referral—the legal issue at hand; and
- the relevant legal standard of capacity.

As noted in the Veterans Administration's *Assessment of Competency and Capacity of the Older Adult: A Practice Guideline for Psychologists,*

There is always a specific reason why the psychologist is being consulted, and it is often not clearly stated. The psychologist must also understand the circumstances under which the person is allegedly unable to function under legal standards for competency. What specific areas of skill and function are at issue? In what circumstances and places do they occur? What other resources does the patient have to assist him/her in this matter? Why is the question being asked now? Was there a critical incident? Are there any major changes (e.g., surgery, relocation), which have had or might have a significant impact on this individual's ability to make decisions? (U.S. Department Veterans Affairs, 1997, p. 29).

If the referral letter from the lawyer does not include these elements, the clinician should seek the information. It is important for the clinician to communicate with the lawyer orally, as well as receiving a written request, to make sure there is a clear understanding of the purpose for the referral and the elements outlined in the referral letter, as noted in the checklist on this page. The aim is to ensure a complete and well-targeted assessment that is worth the money spent. Having to fill in gaps or ambiguities afterwards is both costly and an inefficient use of everyone's time.

How Will the Lawyer Use Your Report?

Ultimately, the judgment about the client's capacity for the legal transaction at hand is the lawyer's to make. While the results of a clinical assessment generally will be a determining factor, client capacity to accomplish a legal task is a *legal decision* and an inherent part of the lawyer-client relationship. Thus, the lawyer can use the assessment report as valuable—often conclusive—evidence, but still needs to "look behind" the report and make an independent judgment taking all factors into account. Ideally, the lawyer will use the capacity assessment in his or her own evaluation, including the steps outlined in the ABA-APA capacity assessment *Handbook for Lawyers* (ABA Commission on Law and Aging et al., 2005, pp.13 - 26).

Once the lawyer has used the psychologist's report in making a legal judgment about the capacity of a client, the report is subject to multiple applications. The lawyer may:

- Maintain it in the file as evidence to support the lawyer's determination about capacity;
- Use it as formal evidence in a judicial proceeding;
- Use it to help frame judicial orders for a limited guardianship or conservatorship in which the individual retains powers in areas of retained capacity;
- Take protective action as allowed under the ethical rules for lawyers who have clients with diminished capacity and who are at risk of harm; or
- Recommend to the client and family clinical interventions, placements or changes in lifestyle, based on the report, before pursuing any legal transactions.

Are Third Party Observers of Evaluations a Good Idea?

Sometimes the lawyer may request to be present during a formal evaluation, or demand that a third party be present to observe the testing. The lawyer's aim is to ensure that the test and questions are fair to the client and that the test procedures are accurately administered. The presence of third party observers in psychological evaluations has been controversial; and the topic has triggered position papers by professional organizations and court decisions.

The presence of a third party observer may affect the client's performance and introduce distractions and other variables that deviates from the standard testing procedure. Standardized test manuals (Anastasi 1988;

McSweeny et al 1998; APA CPTA Guidelines, 2007) The presence of a third party observer "may represent a threat to the validity and reliability of the data generated by an examination conducted under these circumstances, and may compromise the valid use of normative data in interpreting test scores" (NAN, 1999). APA's *Statement on Third Party Observers in Psychological Testing and Assessment* (2007) provides further information, including situations in which a third party's presence may enhance validity (e.g., translator, caregivers in some situations).

The U.S. Supreme Court has stated that the presence of an attorney during an evaluation "could contribute little and might seriously disrupt the examination" (*Estelle v. Smith,* 451 U.S. 454, 470 n. 14, 1981). However, it should be noted that case law on third party observation varies. For example, in Florida a recent criminal case, *Maraman v State of Florida* (980 So.2s 1096 (2008), held that a defendant who raised an insanity defense to murder charge was entitled to have an examination by a clinical psychologist videotaped. The court referred to the state's "liberal policy governing the attendance of third persons at examinations in adversarial settings" and found that "a person who is required to submit to a mental examination in an adversarial proceeding or setting is entitled to have the examination attended by her attorney and a court reporter or videographer, subject to the court's authority to limit attendance for good cause. "

If an attorney request third party observation, it is important for the clinician to make the lawyer aware of the potential for altered test results, and the statements by national clinical organizations. If the attorney insists on the observation, the psychologist may decline to conduct the evaluation, could alter testing procedures to minimize the intrusion, or consider other options outlined in the APA statement.

Working with the Court in Judicial Proceedings, Including Guardianship

In addition to receiving referrals from lawyers, psychologists sometimes are involved in court proceedings. Psychologists may give depositions or be called to testify in court as an expert in capacity assessment in a range of judicial settings, including adult guardianship cases.

Psychologists in Court

Capacity can become a key focus in litigation—for example, in a will contest when the capacity of the testator is at issue; in a dispute about medical treatment in which the ability to give informed consent is questioned; or in civil litigation in which contractual capacity is a factor. Psychologists can make important contributions, providing essential evidence in such cases. Judges will frequently rely on the statement of a psychologist in making tough decisions about the capacity of an individual to perform a specific task. Whether giving a sworn deposition or being called to court as an expert witness, psychologists should be prepared to establish their qualifications in capacity evaluation. In court, you may be examined by the opposing attorney about your credentials, the depth and currency of your knowledge, the evaluation of the individual, and your opinion as to capacity. Be prepared! An excellent reference is Brodsky (1991), *Testifying in Court: Guidelines and Maxims for the Expert Witness,* as well as additional resources by Brodsky (Brodsky, 1991; 2004). He explains:

> For the past 20 years I have been leading workshops for mental health professionals about testifying in court. What I have learned is that for some potential expert witnesses, the prospect of ever testifying in court is frightening. For other witnesses, a particular kind of case is difficult . . . . For still other expert witnesses, testifying is a time of professional mastery, occasionally elation, a chance to explain and defend their knowledge in a public forum.

Brodsky gives 62 maxims to help potential expert witnesses prepare and to respond to cross-examination. For example:

- "Review current literature on the topic about which you will testify." The references in this handbook should be a good start.

- "Witnesses often feel like aliens in the courtroom. The solution is to be present often and to develop a sense of place identity." He advises going into the empty courtroom alone and sitting for a while or sitting in on other trials.
- "Meet with the attorney prior to the direct examination and be involved in preparing the questions."
- "Prepare a list of professionally relevant and complete qualifying questions for the attorney to use in the opening of the direct examination." If challenged, "comfortably agree with accurate challenges to your credentials. Offer narrative explanations only when they are non-defensive and unforced."
- What if you make a mistake? "After a disaster during testimony, correct the error as soon as you can. If you cannot, let it go."
- You may get a question about "examiner effects"—the influences a psychological examiner has on a client. "Cross-examinations about examiner effects call for the witness to explain how training and standardized procedures diminish such effects."

Brodsky and similar sources give additional tips for expert witnesses to help you amplify the points in your evaluation and give the court an accurate picture of the strengths and weaknesses of the alleged incapacitated person.

Be Prepared to Testify in Court

- Review relevant literature.
- Become familiar with the courtroom.
- Work with the attorney prior to direct examination.
- Don t be defensive.

Guardianship Proceedings

The remainder of this section concerns the role of psychologists in evaluating an alleged incapacitated individual in an *adult guardianship proceeding.* Such proceedings will become increasingly more frequent in the coming years as t as the aging of the population and the number of old-old increases, and the number of individuals with Alzheimer's disease rises, and the population of younger adults with intellectual disabilities rises.

What Is "Incapacity" in Guardianship Law? Guardianship is a relationship created by state law in which a court gives one person or entity (the guardian) the duty and power to make personal and/or property decisions for another (the ward or incapacitated person). The appointment of a guardian occurs when a judge decides an adult individual lacks capacity to make decisions on his or her own behalf (Quinn, 2005). Each state has an adult guardianship statute providing for a specific process and procedural protections for the alleged incapacitated individual. State terminology varies. Under the Uniform Guardianship and Protective Proceedings Act and a growing number of state laws, a "guardian" makes personal decisions concerning health care, living arrangement, and lifestyle; while a "conservator" makes financial and property decisions—but some states use different terms. For example, the law might refer to a "guardian of the person" and "guardian of property"—or a "conservator" might encompass both, as in California. (See Glossary at Appendix A.)

Each state law sets out a definition of incapacity. As outlined in Chapter 3, these definitions have changed over time, moving from medical labels—often including archaic discriminatory terms such as "senility" and "imbecility"—toward a four-pronged approach including: (1) medical condition; (2) cognitive impairment; (3) functional ability; and (4) risk of harm. State laws combine various of these elements as guidance for judges in determining the capacity of an adult against whom a petition for guardianship has been brought.

Statutes in the vast majority of states provide for a clinical examination as evidence of incapacity, and some 31 state laws specifically include a psychologist in the range of clinical experts (Teaster, Wood, Schmidt & Lawrence,

2007; see chart of Hurme et al., 2006). (Other examiners named by state statutes include physicians, psychiatrists, mental health professionals, social workers, nurses and "other qualified professionals.") In approximately 30 states a clinical examination is required, while some 15 states leave this to the discretion of the judge, and the remainder of states give no statutory direction (Mayhew, 2005; Moye, Wood, Edelstein, Armesto, Harrison, Bower & Wood, 2007; Moye, Butz, Marson, & Wood, 2007).

The Uniform Guardianship and Protective Proceedings Act, which serves as a model for state legislation, calls for examination by "a physician, psychologist, or other individual appointed by the court who is qualified to evaluate the respondent's alleged impairment." (Uniform Guardianship and Protective Proceedings Act, 1997). A growing number of states provide for a comprehensive, interdisciplinary team approach—such as an evaluation by a physician, psychologist, and social worker.

What Can a Guardianship Capacity Evaluation Include? Clinical evaluation is critical to the judge's determination of capacity and appointment of a guardian. However, historically assessments frequently have been limited. Sometimes a clinician simply and briefly states a conclusion about capacity, rather than offering a detailed and nuanced description of the findings. Indeed, a 2006 study examined clinical evidence of guardianship in three states, rating evaluations on diagnosis, prognosis, cognitive or psychiatric symptoms, functional abilities, values or preferences, and social system. The study found that many of these elements often were missing; and over 28% of the files included conclusory comments without supporting statements or documentation (Moye et al., 2007). Such a conclusory letter may be of little value to the judge in fashioning a guardianship order (Bulcroft, Kielkopf, & Tripp, 1991; Dudley & Goins, 2003; Moye, et al, 2007). Without a clear picture of the individual, the judge will be working in the dark in trying to make an informed, fair, and tailored decision

about the person's capacity and the intervention necessary.

The practice of submitting a conclusory or "short shrift" statement may be due to lack of direction from statute or from the court as to the format, content, and scope of the assessment— or lack of conceptual models and instruments for assessing capacity in guardianship. If clinicians provide information on all of the nine elements in the model set out in Chapter 3 in reports submitted to court in guardianship proceedings, the quality of information judges have before them will be greatly enhanced.

In addition, clinicians should be aware of any statutory guidance concerning the information needed in a clinical assessment. Statutes in 23 states offer such guidance (Mayhew, 2005). Court rules and court orders also may specify the elements of an evaluation.

The court also may direct the clinician to indicate whether the individual can attend the hearing, and if so, what accommodations should be considered. The individual has a right to be present, and the court must provide reasonable accommodations under the Americans with Disabilities Act. About half of the state laws and Uniform Act *require* that the person be present unless good cause is shown (for more information refer to your state statute). Often people may want their "day in court" and feel more satisfaction from the hearing if they are present and involved, whether a guardian is appointed or not. Additionally, presence in court allows the judge an opportunity to observe the individual. The person may or may not become a witness in the case. However, a medical

---

Doing a capacity assessment for guardianship? Check three sources of guidance:

1. The nine-element model set out in Chapter 3;
2. Any statutory provisions or court rules on assessment elements; and
3. The court s or party s request for assessment.

condition may prevent presence—or the person may not wish to come.

It is useful when the psychologist's report:

- Makes the judge aware of any possible *reversible causes* of impairment—such as delirium, depression, or the effects of medications.
- Indicates any possible *mitigating factors* that might be masquerading as impairment—such as hearing loss, grief, malnutrition, or educational or cultural barriers.

- Indicates any possible *less restrictive alternatives* to guardianship. For example, perhaps the individual maintains the ability to execute a health care advance directive or a financial power of attorney.

> Consider any less restrictive alternatives, see **Appendix F.**

Is the Evaluation Request from Court or From Parties to the Proceeding? The role of the psychologist may differ depending on whether the evaluation is ordered by the court or is requested by the petitioner or the respondent.

The *court may order* an evaluation at any stage of the proceeding, if additional clinical input is needed. Many courts have specific forms for the evaluator to complete. The form may or may not lend itself to inclusion of all of the handbook elements and the additional information helpful to the judge. A cover letter or a more extensive attachment may be permitted, allowing for further specificity. The ABA-APA "Model Clinical Evaluation Report" is a tool that may be helpful to clinicians in completing the report (available in the ABA-APA judges handbook: www.apa.org/pi/aging). For the court-ordered evaluation payment may come from the estate of the alleged incapacitated person, from the court budget—or in specific instances may be covered by Medicare, Medicaid or private insurance.

The psychologist needs to consider the consent of the individual for the evaluation.

State law may address the right to refuse to participate in an evaluation. As with attorney referrals, practically, there can be no evaluation unless the individual at some level agrees to participate in the interview and the assessment tests. The clinician could wait for a time in which the person is stabilized, explain the assessment, and seek at least an "assent."

A different scenario arises if one of the parties—the *petitioner or the respondent— requests* a statement for the guardianship petition or hearing, or requests the release of a letter or statement previously prepared from an evaluation prior to the petition. The party may supply the psychologist with the court form for clinical statements—or simply may request a letter or statement to be attached to the petition or submitted to the court. The clinician should seek to include the same elements discussed above, offering a thorough capacity analysis. The clinician would have similar concerns in seeking the individual's consent. If the request is for release of an earlier report or statement, consider whether it is still timely and accurate or needs to be supplemented with more current information.

> What does a limited order look like?
> What does a guardianship plan look like?
> For examples, refer to the ABA-APA
> Handbook for Judges at:
> http://www.apa.org/pi/aging/capacity_judges_handbook.pdf

It is important for psychologists to understand that HIPAA (1996) differs depending on whether the evaluation is ordered by the court or requested by the petitioner. If a court orders the evaluation, there are no barriers under HIPAA in providing the results to the judge, since under federal regulations, a "covered entity," including a psychologist, may disclose protected health information to comply with a court order, as long as the disclosure is limited to the protected health information expressly authorized by the order (45 C.F.R. 164.512(e)(1)(i)) (You do not have to disclose your informal psychotherapy notes). The psychologist needs to explain to the individual that patient-therapist confidentiality does not apply when a court orders the evaluation. However, if the information is requested by the petitioner, HIPAA protections come into play, and any disclosure would require the authorization of the individual.

How Will the Court and Guardian Use Your Report? Your evaluation report frequently will be the key piece of evidence on which the judge will rely in making a decision about the capacity of the individual and the need for appointment of a guardian. Judges typically don't have training in mental health or psychology, and look to expert advice on which to base their judicial opinion. Because guardianship removes fundamental rights it is incumbent on psychologists to offer an informed and thorough assessment.

In addition to determining whether a guardian is needed, the judge decides the scope of the guardianship order. A full or "plenary" guardianship transfers all rights and powers of the individual to the court-appointed guardian, reducing the person to the status of a child— except for any remaining rights preserved by statute. A *limited guardianshi p* transfers rights and powers only in those areas in which the judge determines the person lacks capacity. The principle underlying limited guardianship is that there is no "bright line" of capacity—that incapacity need not be all or nothing.

In 1982, the Uniform Guardianship and Protective Proceedings Act included limited guardianship provisions, giving a major boost to adoption of the concept in state law. Today virtually all state guardianship statutes include provisions for limiting or tailoring the court order—in some cases stating a preference for limited guardianship over plenary guardianship—and most include language acknowledging the importance of "maximizing self-determination and independence" of the individual.

Such language on limited guardianship, however, is difficult to put into practice. A 1994 study found that nationwide the overall rate for use of limited guardianships (excluding one high-use state) was about 5% (Center for Social Gerontology, 1994)—and while there are no recent statistics, usage appears low. Limited guardianship requires that the judge tailor each order to fit the specific areas of ability of the individual. A legal scholar postulated that:

> Judges are not like baseball umpires, calling strikes and balls or merely labeling someone competent or incompetent. Rather, the better analogy is that of a craftsman who carves staffs from tree branches. Although the end result—a wood staff—is similar, the process of creation is distinct to each staff. Just as the good wood-carver knows that within each tree branch there is a unique staff that can be "released" by the acts of the carver, so, too, a good judge understands that, within the facts surrounding each guardianship petition, there is an outcome that will best serve the needs of the incapacitated person, if only the judge and the litigants can find it (Frolik, 2002).

Your evaluation report is the key tool that may enable a judge to craft such a nuanced order. Ultimately, the shape and extent of the guardianship order—and the resulting retention or removal of individual rights—hinges on the quality of information provided by the clinician and others who testify to the individual's abilities.

After the judge's determination and order, a psychologist's evaluation report may have an additional use—in guiding a plan to be followed by the court-appointed guardian.

A *guardianship plan* is a forward-looking document submitted by a guardian to the court describing the proposed care of the individual and reporting on past care. Guardianship plans provide a baseline inventory that enables the court to measure the guardian's future performance. Some state statutes include requirements for guardianship plans. In other cases, court practice may provide for the filing of such plans. A 2005 AARP survey showed that close to 35% of responding guardianship experts said their court requires guardians to file forward-looking plans (Karp & Wood, 2006).

IX. Emerging Issues

The past ten years has witnessed a tremendous growth in the attention to capacity issues as they affect older populations. While this book has focused on six of the more common reasons for referrals for civil capacity assessment of older adults, a number of other areas represent "emerging issues" in capacity assessment that are receiving increasing attention in the scientific, legal, and clinical literature.

Capacity to Participate in Mediation

"Dispute resolution" encompasses a broad range of processes designed to assist parties in resolving differences. While court adjudication is one form of dispute resolution, it also encompasses other alternatives such as arbitration, mediation, conciliation, and use of ombudsman programs. Dispute resolution is a broad-based, rapidly growing movement touching all sectors of society, including government, business, labor, schools, consumer affairs, and the family.

> For more on dispute resolution, see the ABA Section on Dispute Resolution www.abanet.org/dispute/home.html and the Association for Conflict Resolution www.acrnet.org

Mediation—one prominent form of dispute resolution—is a process in which a trained neutral facilitator assists disputants in framing issues in dispute, enhances communication between parties, helps parties develop possible solutions, and aids them in reaching mutually acceptable agreements (Nolan-Haley, 1992; see also www.mediate.com). The process is voluntary, involving a willingness of the parties to "come to the table" with a mediator present, and to discuss the issues. The goal in mediation is less "to win" than to reach a negotiated agreement that reflects the interests of the parties involved. The solutions are crafted by the parties themselves, and can be more creative and more suited to individual needs than might be possible through court litigation or the third party decisions of an arbitrator. Because the parties have an "ownership" in the agreement, they may have a sense of empowerment from their involvement and may be more likely to abide by the terms of the agreement. Yet there can be risks that inappropriate use of mediation could stifle an individual's rights under law.

There are hundreds of community mediation programs, court-annexed mediation programs, and mediation practitioners throughout the nation. *Elder mediation* is a growing field in which meditative techniques are applied to conflicts in areas such as adult guardianship, bioethics, housing, consumer affairs, intergenerational differences, disability disputes and long-term care conflicts (Wood, 2001). The benefits of mediation in such contexts can be significant, as mediation can offer a convenient, timely, inexpensive, and empowering approach toward solving difficult problems.

Sometimes issues of capacity arise in elder mediation settings. Mediation is premised on the notion that the disputing parties understand the problem at issue and the process for resolution. The mediator must determine whether the parties have capacity to participate in the process, always beginning with a presumption of capacity. According to the Americans with Disabilities Act (ADA) *Mediation Guidelines,* the mediator should determine a party's capacity "on a case by case basis," if and when a question arises concerning ability to engage in the process and ability to "give voluntary and informed consent to any agreement reached." The *Guidelines* name several factors in the determination: "The mediator should ascertain that a party understands the nature of the mediation process, who the parties are, the role of the mediator, the parties' relationship to the mediator, and the issues at hand." The *Guidelines* caution that this determination should not "rely solely on a party's medical condition or diagnosis" and that "an adjudication of legal incapacity is not necessarily determinative of capacity to mediate" (Americans with Disabilities Act *Mediation Guidelines*, 2000).

Mediation experts Coy and Hedeen (1998) name eight "minimal requirements" for participation in community mediation, including the ability to: (1) see how specific issues are related and connected to each other; (2) focus on one issue at a time; (3) understand cause and effect, match events and consequences; (4) take responsibility for one's own actions; (5) conceive of and respond to common measures of time in the context of scheduling; (6) comprehend the nature of a behavioral commitment; (7) identify desired outcomes; and (8) understand the mediator's role.

Determining capacity of parties in mediation, just as in other contexts, can be difficult and ambiguous. Coy and Hedeen suggest that mediators should not be hasty in making judgments about lack of capacity, and submit that the dangers of "rushing too quickly to judgment" must be balanced with the integrity of the mediation process. They caution against overly strict screening criteria and "raising the bar too high" so as to exclude parties from the opportunities of mediation. The real question might not be "can the party mediate" but "can the party mediate with support?" Mediators need to consider critical accommodations, such as including a support person for a person with possible diminished capacity; changing the time, length, or setting of the mediation session; allowing for frequent breaks; and checking understanding with paraphrasing.

If a mediator determines that a party is simply unable to participate and adhere to an agreement, the next question is whether a surrogate can participate on behalf of the individual (Karp et al., 1997). The knotty problem of capacity to mediate was highlighted in the *First National Symposium on Ethical Standards for Elder Mediation* in 2007 (Montgomery County Mediation Center et al., 2007) and resulted in significant debate.

At some point a mediator may need guidance on assessing mediation capacity, and may turn to a psychologist. Psychologists must understand the nature of mediation, and provide an evaluation—either informal or formal—about the person's ability to understand the process and issues at hand, make and abide by an agreement. Also, psychologists will need to differentiate the capacity to mediate from conflict avoidance, culturally-based behaviors, or other factors not related to capacity. There are few screening tools to assess capacity to mediate, but there are resources that might provide some initial guideposts for consideration (Coy et al., 1998; Karp et al., 1997). Interested psychologists may wish to identify mediators or mediation programs in advance and develop a working relationship.

Capacity to Consent to Participate in Research Studies

Psychologists may be asked to evaluate an individual's capacity to consent to a research project, particularly those that emphasize the inclusion of patients with neurological conditions, such as Alzheimer's disease, or psychiatric diagnoses, such as schizophrenia, all of which may involve some clinically relevant cognitive impairment. However, these types of issues could arise as part of a variety of studies that include older adults as participants, including those with any potential cognitive impairment.

Capacity to provide informed consent for research participation depends on the complexity of the study in question. That is, a person may have capacity to make an informed decision about a simple low-risk study, such as one that requires a paper and pencil interview, but not have sufficient capacity to make an informed decision about a study involving more complex procedures, such as surgery. As a result, psychologists may be called on to evaluate prospective enrollees in research involving potentially invasive procedures, such as a lumbar puncture in a clinical trial. In most cases, the Institutional Review Board responsible for overseeing the research study will provide guidance on how to handle the consenting procedures for "decisionally impaired" participants; however, these procedures do not provide much direction in terms of *defining decisional impairment*, so that the specifics of that determination may be left up to the psychologist.

Two recent reviews describe instruments for medical and research consent capacity, such as the MacArthur Competence Assessment Tool - CR (Dunn, Nowrangi, Palmer, Jeste, & Saks, 2006; Sturman, 2005). However, for psychologists, it is important to understand that capacity to consent to research participation differs from treatment capacity in several fundamental ways. First, and perhaps most significant, the research study is not for the participant's personal medical benefit. Rather, it is intended to advance knowledge and science. In contrast, treatment is always meant to benefit the individual's medical status. Second, there may be a conflict of interest within the research setting that is not present in the treatment setting. Specifically, the principal investigator of the research study may benefit from increased numbers of study enrollees, whereas this conflict is not likely to occur in a treatment situation. Third, federal regulations mandate what must be disclosed when obtaining informed consent for research participation, and these regulations, which are monitored by the study's local Institutional Review Board, vary depending on the level of risk involved in the research study.

If the psychologist is called upon to make a determination about decisional capacity in a research context, it is important that he or she be knowledgeable about relations between capacity to make an informed decision about research participation and cognitive functioning. Older adults with clinically relevant cognitive impairment, such as Alzheimer's disease, have a reduced ability to provide informed consent for participating in research (Karlawish, Casarett, & James, 2002; Kim, Caine, Currier, Leibovici, & Ryan, 2001). A recent study suggests that older individuals with mild cognitive impairment, a syndrome with circumscribed cognitive impairment but relatively preserved instrumental activities of daily living (such as medication management), may have more difficulties providing informed consent for complicated clinical trials than cognitively normal older adults (Jefferson, et al., 2008). However, it is important to remember that decisional capacity is situation-specific, and cognitive impairment or a neurological diagnosis does not mean that a person automatically has impaired research consent capacity (Marson, Schmitt, Ingram, & Harrell, 1994). Among patients with schizophrenia, psychiatric symptoms are generally not predictive of decisional capacity (Palmer & Salva, 2007). In bipolar disorder, manic symptoms may decrease the capacity to consent to research (Misra, Socherman, Park, Hauser, & Ganzini, 2008; Palmer, Dunn, Depp, Eyler, & Jeste, 2007). Future research in this area will increase our understanding of the cognitive correlates of research consent capacity across the cognitive aging spectrum and improve specific assessment tools.

In the event that a cognitively impaired individual is unable to provide informed consent, a legally authorized representative may be able to do so. However, the authority of a health care proxy or guardian to consent to research participation is not clearly defined in law. In some states, if the research holds therapeutic benefit, the health care proxy or guardian may be authorized to provide surrogate consent. For example, Utah's healthcare power of attorney statute (§ 75-2a-1106) an individual may make an advance health care directive in which the principal can authorize the agent to consent to participation in medical research. In some states, guardians may be required to seek specific court approval for participation in research. This area of law is likely to evolve.

Capacity to Vote

While voting is a fundamental right protected by both federal and state constitutions, it is balanced in law by a need to protect the integrity of the electoral process. State constitutions, election laws, and guardianship laws all contribute to a complex matrix of voting rights for individuals with cognitive impairments. States have authority to regulate the election process, including defining who is eligible to vote (Hurme & Applebaum, 2007). Federal election law allows states to disenfranchise persons "by reason of mental incapacity" (42 U.S.C. & 1973 gg-6 (a) (3) (B) (2000) primarily to protect the electoral process from fraud and incompetent voting. The clear majority of states have no disenfranchisement provision for persons with a category of mental impairment or disability (Hurme et al., 2007). Specific state elections laws vary widely in their descriptions of these provisions. In a few states, including Massachusetts, the right to vote is automatically revoked if an individual is placed by probate courts as "under guardianship." In other states, the right to vote may be addressed during guardianship proceedings. Because the right to vote can not be delegated, an individual under guardianship law either has the right to vote or has lost it (Hurme et al., 2007).

The guardianship reform movement has resulted in changes to most state laws that now encourage the crafting of limited versus full guardianships where it is at all possible (see Chapter 2). Fortunately, these reforms are now being adopted for voting rights. For example, a growing number of states have specific provisions that persons under full or limited guardianships retain all legal and civil rights not specifically taken away (Hurme et al., 2007). For psychologists involved in guardianship proceedings, there is an opportunity to protect civil rights by explicitly addressing the client's ability to vote, despite other areas of weakness.

The assessment of voting abilities is controversial and was one of the topics of a recent symposium entitled Facilitating Voting As People Age: Implications of Cognitive Impairment, held in March 2007 at the University of the Pacific McGeorge School of Law.

The recommendations of the symposium included a statement on capacity to vote. The recommendation emphasized that capacity to vote should be presumed, regardless of guardianship status, and that state laws "should explicitly state that the right to vote is retained except by court order" in accordance with procedural standards. The recommendation set out a capacity standard as follows: "If state law permits exclusion of a person from voting on the basis of incapacity, a person should be determined to lack capacity only if the person cannot communicate with or without accommodations a specific desire to participate in the voting process." This relatively low standard presumes the capacity to vote, and is in accordance with a key court determination holding that a state bar to voting by reason of cognitive impairment must only be enforced through a specific judicial finding of an individual's inability to understand the nature

and effect of voting. (*Doe v Rowe*, 156 F. Supp. 2d 35, D. Me., 2001.)

There has been some work on tools to assess ability to vote (e.g., the Competence Assessment Tool for Voting (CAT-V) (Applebaum, 2007). These tools are intended to be used when a court specifically addresses the right to vote (e.g., in a guardianship hearing regarding an individual person) and should not be employed as screening mechanisms at polling booths or in long-term care facilities (Sabatino et al., 2007).

Future Directions

Capacity assessment of older adults will become increasingly common in the coming years. The convergence of several factors—increasing longevity, the increased numbers of adults in the United States reaching old age, along with the increasing prevalence neurocognitive conditions associated with aging, and the tremendous intergenerational transfer of wealth will make capacity assessment a prominent public concern.

Psychologists' expertise in standardized cognitive and functional assessment will be critical in enhancing the accuracy and comprehensiveness of these important assessments that assist clinical and legal professionals in balancing the need to promote autonomy of older adults with the need to protect and provide for those who are vulnerable.

An emerging body of scientific literature has been useful in enhancing the empirical basis of these assessments, while a promising "first generation" of capacity assessment instruments may help to direct evaluators to more domain relevant assessment.

Nevertheless, many areas of civil capacity assessment of older adults remain largely unexamined (e.g., sexual consent), particularly in ways that are readily transferable to clinical assessment in the here and now. Psychologists' expertise in research is needed to advance the field. Many domains of capacity, and the related concept of undue influence, would benefit from studies that focus on development of assessment instruments, as well as related work to define the clinical risk factors associated with capacity loss within neurocognitive or neuropsychiatric conditions.

While additional research is critical to enhancing the empirical basis of this evolving field, clinical capacity opinions will of course remain a professional judgment, informed by the scientific literature and the clinical expertise of the evaluator. As such, ongoing education and training regarding these assessments will continue to be needed.

Capacity is an evolving and complex psycho-legal construct with clinical, ethical, and legal dimensions. Vigorous interdisciplinary collaboration between clinical, legal, and public policy professionals will continue to be vital to advancing the field of capacity assessment, protecting rights, and furthering the accuracy and utility of capacity assessment in resolving important issues of autonomy and protection for the growing population of older adults.

X. References

Administration on Aging. (2006). *A profile of older Americans: 2006.* Washington, DC: Department of Health and Human Services. Retrieved on March 5, 2008, from http://www.aoa.gov/PROF/Statistics/profile/2006/2006profile.pdf.

Allen, R. S., DeLaine, S. R., Chaplin, W. F., Marson, D. C., Bourgeois, M., Dijkstra, K., et al. (2003). Advance care planning in nursing homes: Correlates of capacity and possession of advance directives. *The Gerontologist, 43*, 309-317.

Alzheimer's Association, (2008) *Alzheimer's Disease Facts and Figures: 10 Million U.S. Baby Boomers Will Develop Alzheimer's Disease.* Retrieved July 7, 2008 from http://www.alz.org/national/documents/report_alzfactsfigures2008.pdf.

American Association of Retired Persons (AARP). (n.d.). *Driver safety.* Retrieved on March 14, 2008, from www.aarp.org/families/driver_safety/

American Bar Association. (2002). *Model rules of professional conduct.* Washington, DC: Author.

American Bar Association Commission on Law, Aging, American Psychological Association, & National College of Probate Judges. (2006). *Judicial determination of capacity of older adults in guardianship proceedings: A handbook for judges..* Washington, DC: Authors.

American Bar Association Commission on Law and Aging & American Psychological Association. (2005). *Assessment of older adults with diminished capacity: A handbook for lawyers.* Washington, DC: Authors.

American Bar Association Commission on the Mentally Disabled & Commission on Legal Problems of the Elderly. (1989). *Guardianship: An agenda for reform, rec. III-A.* Washington, DC: American Bar Association.

American Psychological Association. (2002). *Ethical principles of psychologists and code of conduct.* Washington, DC: Author.

Anderer, S. J. (1990). *Determining competency in guardianship proceedings.* Washington, DC: American Bar Association.

Anderer, S. J. (1997). *Development of an instrument to evaluate the capacity of elderly persons to make personal care and financial decisions.* Unpublished doctoral dissertation, Allegheny University of the Health Sciences.

Anderten, P. (1979). *The elderly, incompetency, and guardianship.* Unpublished master's thesis, St Louis University.

Appelbaum, P. S. (1982). Competency to consent to research: A psychiatric overview. *Archives of General Psychiatry, 39*, 951-958.

Appelbaum, P. S., & Bateman, A. (1980). Empirical assessment of competency to consent to psychiatric hospitalization. *American Journal of Psychiatry, 138*, 1170-1176.

Appelbaum, P. S., & Grisso, T. (1988). Assessing patients' capacities to consent to treatment. *New England Journal of Medicine, 319*, 1635-1638.

Appelbaum, P. S., & Grisso, T. (1995). The MacArthur Treatment Competency Study 1: Mental illness and competence to consent to treatment. *Law and Human Behavior, 19*, 105-126.

Appelbaum, P. S., & Grisso, T. (2001). *MacArthur competence assessment tool for clinical research (MacCAT-CR).* Sarasota, FL: Professional Resource Press.

Appelbaum, P. S., & Roth, L. (1981). Clinical issues in the assessment of competence. *American Journal of Psychiatry, 138*, 1462-1467.

Appelbaum, P. S., Bonnie, R.J.; & Karlawish, J.H. (2005). The capacity to vote in people with Alzheimer's disease. *American Journal of Psychiatry, 16*, 1094-2100.

Azad, N., Byszewski, A, Amos, S., & Molnar, F. (2002). A survey of the impact of driving cessation on older drivers. *Geriatrics Today, 5*, 170-174.

Ball, K. K., Roenker, D. L., & Bruni, J. R. (1990). Developmental changes in attention and visual search throughout adulthood. In J. Enns (Ed.), *Advances in Psychology* (pp. 489-508). Amsterdam, Netherlands: North-Holland-Elsevier Science Publishers.

Ball, K. K, Roenker, D. L, Wadley, V. G., Edwards, J. D., Roth, D. L., McGwin, G., Raleigh, R., Joyce, J.J., Cissell, G.M., & Dube, T. (2006). Can high-risk older drivers be identified through performance-based measures in a department of motor vehicles setting? *Journal of the American Geriatrics Society, 54*, 77-84.

Barton, C. D., Mallik, H. S., Orr, W. B., & Janofsky, J. S. (1996). Clinicians' judgment of capacity of nursing home patients to give informed consent. *Psychiatric Services, 47*, 956-960.

Beach, M. C., Roter, D. L., Wang, N. Y., Duggan, P. S., & Cooper, L. A. (2006). Are physicians' attitudes of respect accurately perceived by patients and associated with more positive communication behaviors? *Patient Education and Counseling, 62,* 347-354.

Bean, G., Nishiasato, S., Rector, M. A., & Glancy, G. (1994). The psychometric properties of the competency interview schedule. *Canadian Journal of Psychiatry, 39*, 368-376.

Beck, R. S., Daughtridge, R., & Sloane, P. (2002). Physician-patient communication in the primary care office: A systematic review. *Journal American Board of Family Practice, 15*, 25-38.

Benjamin N. Cardozo School of Law. (2000). Americans with Disabilities (ADA) Mediation Guidelines. Retrieved May 1, 2008, from http://www.cojcr.org/ada.html.

Berg, J. W., Appelbaum, P. S., Lidz, C. W., & Parker, L. S. (2001). *Informed consent: Legal theory and clinical practice*. New York: Oxford.

Bharucha, A. J., Panday, R., Shen, C., Dodge, H. H., & Ganguli, M. (2004). Predictors of nursing facility admission: A 12-year epidemiological study in the United States. *Journal of the American Geriatrics Society, 52*, 434-439.

Blackhall, L. J., Murphy, S. T., Frank, G., Michel, V., & Azen, S. (1995). Ethnicity and attitudes toward patient autonomy. *Journal of the American Medical Association, 274*, 820–825.

Bravo, M., & Nakayama, K. (1992). The role of attention in visual search tasks. *Perceptual Psychophysiology, 51*, 465-472.

Brodsky, S. (1991). *Testifying in court: Guidelines and maxims for the expert witness*. Washington, DC: American Psychological Association.

Brodsky, S. (2004). *Coping With Cross-Examination and Other Pathways to Effective Testimony* Washington, DC: American Psychological Association.

Bulcroft, K., Kielkopf, M., & Tripp, K. (1991). Elderly wards and their legal guardians: Analysis of county probate records in Ohio and Washington. *The Gerontologist, 31*, 156-164.

Carney, M. T., Neugroschl, J., Morrison, R. S., Marin, D., & Siu, A. L. (2001). The development and piloting of a capacity assessment tool. *The Journal of Clinical Ethics, 12*, 17-23.

Carr, D. B. (2000). The older adult driver. *American Family Physician, 61,*141-148.

Center for Practical Bioethics (2006). Considerations regarding the needs of long term care residents for intimate relationships and sexual activity. Kansas City, MO: Center for Practical Bioethics.

Center for Social Gerontology. (1994). *National study of guardianship systems: Findings and recommendations*. Ann Arbor, MI: Author.

Clemens, E., & Hayes, H.E. (1997). Assessing and balancing elderly risk, safety and autonomy: decision making practices of elder care workers. *Home Health Care Services Quarterly, 16*, 3-20.

Cohen, C. I., Cohen, G. D., Blank, K., Gaitz, C., Katz, I. R., Leuchter, A., Maletta, G., Meyers, B., Sakauye, K., & Shamoian, C. (2000). Schizophrenia and older adults: An overview. *American Journal of Geriatric Psychiatry, 8*, 19-28.

Collopy, B. J. (1988). Autonomy in long term care: Some crucial distinctions. *The Gerontologist 28*, Supplement, 10-17.

Cooper, L. A., Roter, D. L., Johnson, R. L., Ford, D. E., Steinwachs, D. M., & Powe, N. R. (2003). Patient-centered communication, ratings of care, and concordance of patient and physician race. *Annals Internal Medicine, 139*, 907-915.

Coy, P. & Hedeen, T. (1998). Disabilities and mediation readiness in court-referred cases: Developing screening criteria and service networks. *Mediation Quarterly, 16,* 1998-99.

Dellinger, A. M., Sehgal, M., Sleet, D. A., & Barrett-Connor, E. (2001). Driving cessation: What older former drivers tell us. *Journal of American Geriatrics Society, 49,* 431-435.

Depp, C. A., & Jeste, D. V. (2004). Bipolar disorder in older adults: A critical review. *Bipolar Disorders, 6,* 343-367.

Ditto, P. H., Druley, J. A., Moore, K. A., Danks, J. H., & Smucker, W. D. (1996). Fates worse than death: The role of valued life activities in health state evaluations. *Health Psychology, 15,* 332-343.

Doukas, D., & McCullough, L. (1991). The values history: The evaluation of the patient's values and advance directives. *Journal of Family Practice, 32,* 145–153.

Doe v. Rowe. 156 F. Supp. 2d 35 (D. Me. 2001).

Drane, J. F. (1984). Competency to give an informed consent: A model for making clinical assessments. *Journal of the American Medical Association, 252,* 925–927.

Dudley, K., & Goins, R. T. (2003). Guardianship capacity evaluations of older adults: Comparing current practice to legal standards in two states. *Journal of Aging and Social Policy, 15,* 97-115.

Dunn, L. B., & Jeste, D. V. (2001). Enhancing informed consent for research and treatment. *Neuropsychopharmacology, 24,* 595-607.

Dunn, L. B., Nowrangi, M. A., Palmer, B. W., Jeste, D. V., & Saks, E. R. (2006). Assessing decisional capacity for clinical research or treatment: A review of instruments. *American Journal of Psychiatry, 163,* 1323.

Dymek, M. P., Atchison, P., Harrell, L., & Marson, D. C. (2001). Competency to consent to medical treatment in cognitively impaired patients with Parkinson's disease. *Neurology, 56,* 17-24.

Earnst, K., Marson, D., & Harrell, L. (2000). Cognitive models that predict physicians' legal standard and personal judgments of competency in patients with Alzheimer's disease. *Journal of the American Geriatrics Society, 48,* 919-927.

Edelstein, B., Woodhead, E., Segal, D. L., Heisel, M. J., Bower, E. H., Lowery, A. J., & Stoner, S. A. (2008). Older adult psychological assessment: Current instrument status and other considerations. *Clinical Gerontologist,30,* 1-35.

Etchells, E., Darzins, P., Silberfeld, M., Singer, P. A., McKenny, J., Naglie, G., Katz, M., Guyatt, G.H., Molloy, D.W., & Strang D. (1999). Assessment of patients capacity to consent to treatment. *Journal of General Internal Medicine, 14,* 27-34.

Fischer, G. S, Alpert, H. R, Stoeckle, J. D, & Emanuel, L. L. (1997). Can goals of care be used to predict intervention preferences in an advance directive? *Archives of Internal Medicine, 157,* 801-807.

Fiske, A., & O'Riley, A. (2008). Assessment of depression in late life. In J. D. Hunsley & E. J. Mash (Eds.), *A guide to assessments that work.* New York, NY: Oxford University Press.

Fitten, L. J., Lusky, R., & Hamann, C. (1990). Assessing treatment decision-making capacity in elderly nursing home residents. *Journal of the American Geriatrics Society, 38,* 1097-1104.

Fitten, L. J., & Waite, M. S. (1990). Impact of medical hospitalization on treatment decision making capacity in the elderly. *Archives of Internal Medicine, 150,* 1717-1721.

Foley, D. J., Harley, K., Heimovitz, H. K., Guralnik, J. M., & Brock, D. B. (2002). Driving life expectancy of persons aged 70 years and older in the United States. *American Journal of Public Health, 92,* 1284-89.

Frolik, L. (1981). Plenary guardianship: An analysis, a critique and a proposal for reform. *Arizona Law Review, 23,* 599-660.

Frolik, L. (2002). Promoting judicial acceptance and use of limited guardianship. *Stetson Law Review, 31,* 735-755.

Furrow, B. R., Greaney, T. L., Johnson, S. H., Jost, T. S., Schwartz, R. L. (2000). *The doctrine of informed consent* (2nd ed.). St. Paul, MN: Thomson-West.

Ganzini, L., Volicer, L., Nelson, W., & Derse, A. (2003). Pitfalls in assessment of decision-making capacity. *The Academy of Psychosomatic Medicine, 44*, 237-243.

Garner, B. A. (Ed.) (2004). *Black's Law Dictionary,* 8th ed. Eagan, MN: Thomson-West.

Gaugler, J. E., Edwards, A. B., Femia, E. E., Zarit, S. H., Stephens, M. P., Townsend, A., & Greene, R. (2000). Predictors of institutionalization of cognitively impaired elders: Family help and the timing of placement. *The Journal of Gerontology Series B: Psychological Sciences and Social Sciences, 55*, 247-255.

Glass, T.A. (1998). Conjugating the "tenses" of function: Discordance among hypothetical, experimental, and enacted function in older adults. *Gerontologist, 38*, 101-112.

Graber, M. L., Franklin, N., & Gordon, R. (2005). Diagnostic error in internal medicine. *Archives of Internal Medicine, 165*, 1493-1499.

Greiffenstein, M. (1996). The neuropsychological autopsy. *Michigan Bar Journal*, 424-425.

Griffith, H.R., Belue, K., Sicola, A., Krzywanski, S., Zamrini, E., Harrell, L, & Marson, D.C.(2003). Impaired financial abilities in mild cognitive impairment: A direct assessment approach. *Neurology, 60*, 449-457.

Grisso, T. (1986). *Evaluating competencies.* NY: Plenum.

Grisso, T. (2003). *Evaluating competencies: Forensic assessments and instruments* (2nd ed.). New York: Kluwer Academic.

Grisso, T., & Appelbaum, P. S. (1995). Comparison of standards for assessing patients' capacities to make treatment decisions. *American Journal of Psychiatry, 152*, 1033-1037.

Grisso, T., & Applebaum, P. S. (1998). *Assessing Competence to Consent to Treatment.* New York: Oxford University Press.

Groopman, J. (2007). *How doctors think.* New York: Houghton-Mifflin.

Gurrera, R. J., Moye, J., Karel, M. J., Azar, A. R., & Armesto, J. C. (2006). Cognitive performance predicts treatment decisional abilities in mild to moderate dementia. *Neurology, 66*, 1367-1372.

Hall, J. A., Horgan, T. G., Stein, T. S., & Roter, D. L. (2002). Liking in the physician-patient relationship. *Patient Education and Counseling, 48*, 69-77.

Hammes, B.J., & Briggs, L.A. (2005). Initiating, facilitating, and honoring conversations about future medical care. In J. K. Doka, B. Jennings, & C.A. Corr (Eds.), *Ethical dilemmas at the end of life* (pp. 125-138). Washington, DC: Hospice Foundation of America.

Health Insurance Portability and Accountability Act of 1996 (HIPAA), Pub. L. No. 104-191, 110 stat. 1936.

Hill, R. D., Backman, L., & Fratiglioni, L. (1995). Determinants of functional abilities in dementia. *Journal of the American Geriatrics Society, 43*, 1092-1097.

Hornung, C. A., Eleazer, G. P., Strothers, H. S., Wieland, G. D., Eng, C., McCann, R., & Sapir, M. (1998). Ethnicity and decision-makers in a group of frail older people. *Journal of the American Geriatrics Society, 46*, 280–286.

Hope, T., Keene, J., Gedling, K., Fairburn, C.G., & Jacoby, R. (1999). Predictors of institutionalization for people with dementia living with a carer. *International Journal of Geriatric Psychiatry, 13*, 682-690.

Horstman, P. (1975). Protective services for the elderly: The limits of parens patriae. *Missouri Law Review, 40*, 215-236.

Hurme, S.B. & Applebaum, P.S. (2007). Defining and assessing the capacity to vote: The effect of mental impairment on the rights of voters. *McGeorge Law Review, 38,* 931-1014.

Hurme, S., & Wood, E. (2006). *State adult guardianship legislation: Initiation of guardianship proceedings charts.* Washington, DC: American Bar Association Commission on Law & Aging. Retrieved on March 14, 2008, from: http://www.abanet.org/aging/legislativeupdates/docs/Chart-Initiation-1-07ewsbh.pdf

Hunt, L., Morris, J., Edwards, D. & Wilson, B. (1993). Driving performance in persons with mild senile dementia of the Alzheimer type. Journal *of American Geriatric Society, 41*, 747-52.

Hyndman, D., & Ashburn, A. (2003). People with stroke living in the community: Attention deficits, balance, ADL ability and falls. *Disability and Rehabilitation, 25*, 817-822.

Idaho Code. (1999). § 15-5-101(a)(1).

Janofsky, J. S., McCArthy, R. J., & Folstein, M. F. (1992). The Hopkins competence assessment test: A brief method for evaluating patients' capacity to give informed consent. *Hospital and Community Psychiatry, 43*, 132-135.

Janus, S. S., & Janus, C. L. (1993). *The Janus report on sexual behavior.* New York: Wiley.

Jefferson, A. L., Lambe, S., Moser, D. J., Byerly, L. K., Ozonoff, A., & Karlawish, J. H. (2008). Decisional capacity for research participation among individuals with mild cognitive impairment. *Journal of the American Geriatrics Society, 1236-1243.*

Kane, R. A. (2000). Values and preferences. In R. L. Kane & R. A. Kane (Eds.), *Assessing older persons: Measures, meanings, and practice implications.* (pp. 237-260). New York: Oxford University Press

Karel, M.J. (2000). The assessment of values in medical decision making. *Journal of Aging Studies, 14*, 403-422.

Karel, M. J., & Gatz, M. (1996). Factors influencing life-sustaining treatment decisions in a community sample of families. *Psychology and Aging*, 226-234.

Karel, M. J., Moye, J., Bank, A., & Azar, A. R. (2007). Three methods of assessing values for advance care planning comparing persons with and without dementia. *Journal of Aging and Health, 19*, 123-151.

Karel, M. J., Powell, J., & Cantor, M. (2004). Using a values discussion guide to facilitate communication in advance care planning. *Patient Education and Counseling, 55*, 22-31.

Karlawish, J. H., Bonnie, R.J., Applebaum, P.S., Lykestos, C., James, B., Knopman, D., Patusky, C., Kane, R.A., & Karlan, P. S. (2004). Addressing the ethical, legal, and social issues raised by voting by persons with dementia. *Journal of the American Medical Association, 292*, 1345-1350.

Karlawish, J. H., Casarett, D. J., & James, B. D. (2002). Alzheimer's disease patients' and caregivers' capacity, competency, and reasons to enroll in an early-phase Alzheimer's disease clinical trial. *Journal of the American Geriatrics Society, 50*, 2019-2024.

Karp, N., & Wood, E. (1997). *Keep Talking, Keep Listening: Mediating Nursing Home Care Conflicts.* Washington, DC: American Bar Association Commission on Law and Aging.

Kennedy, C. (1999). Assessing competency to consent to sexual activity in the cognitively impaired population. *Journal of Forensic Neuropsychology, 1*, 17-33.

Kennedy, C., & Niederbuhl, J. (2001). Establishing criteria for sexual consent capacity. *American Journal of Mental Retardation, 106*, 503-510.

Kim, S. Y., & Caine, E. D. (2002). Utility and Limits of the Mini Mental State Examination in Evaluating Consent Capacity in Alzheimer's disease. *Psychiatric Services, 53*, 1322-1324.

Kim, S. Y., Caine, E. D., Currier, G. W., Leibovici, A., & Ryan, J. M. (2001). Assessing the competence of persons with Alzheimer's disease in providing informed consent for participation in research. *The American Journal of Psychiatry, 158*, 712-717.

Kim, S. Y., Karlawish, J. H. T., & Caine, E. D. (2002). Current state of research on decision-making competence of cognitively impaired elderly persons. *American Journal of Geriatric Psychiatry, 10*, 151-165.

Kogan, J., Edelstein, B., & McKee, D. (2000). Assessment of anxiety in older adults: Current status. *Journal of Anxiety Disorders, 14*, 109-132.

Lake v. Cameron. 364 F. 2d 657, 658 (D.C. Cir. 1966).

Lantz, M. L. (2004). Consenting adults: Sexuality in the nursing home. *Clinical Geriatrics, 12*, 33-36.

Lawton, M. P., Moss, M., Hoffman, C., Grant, R., Ten Have, T., & Kleban, M. H. (1999). Health, valuation of life, and the wish to live. *The Gerontologist, 39*, 406-416.

Lee, H. C., Lee, A. H., & Cameron, D. (2003). Validation of a driving simulator by measuring the visual attention skill of older adult drivers. *The American Journal of Occupational Therapy, 57*, 324-28.

Lichtenberg, P.A., & Strzepek, D. M. (1990). Assessments of institutionalized dementia patients' competencies to participate in intimate relationships. *The Gerontologist, 30,* 117-120.

Loeb, P. (1996). *Independent Living Scales.* San Antonio: Psychological Corporation.

Loewenstein, D.A., Amigo, E., Duara, R., Guterman, A., Hurwitz, D., Berkowitz, N., Wilkie, F., Weinberg, G., Black, B., & Gittelman, B. (1989). A new scale for the assessment of functional status in Alzheimer's disease and related disorders. *Journal of Gerontology: Psychological Science, 44,* 114-121.

Ludington, T. P. (1962). Reports of treating physician delivered to litigant's own attorney as subject of pretrial or other disclosure, production, or inspection. *American Law Reports, 82,* 1162.

Lyden, M. (2007). Assessment of sexual consent capacity. *Sexual Disabilities, 25,* 3-20.

Maraman v State of Florida, 980 So.2d 1096 (Fla. 2d DCA 2008).

Margulies, P. (1994). Access, connection, and voice: A contextual approach to representing senior citizens of questionable capacity. *Fordham Law Review, 62,* 1073.

Markson, L. J. (1994). Physician assessment of patient competence. *Journal of the American Geriatric Society, 42,* 1074-1080.

Marottoli, R. A., Mendes de Leon, C. F., Glass, T. A., Williams, C. S., Cooney, L. M., & Berkman, L. F. (2000). Consequences of driving cessation: Decreased out-of-home activity levels. *The Journals of Gerontology. Series B, Psychological sciences and social sciences, 55,* S334-S340.

Marottoli, R. A., Mendes de Leon, C. F., Glass, T. A., Williams, C. S., Cooney, L. M., Berkman, L. F., & Tinetti, M. (1997). Driving cessation and increased depressive symptoms: Prospective evidence from the New Haven EPESE. *Journal of the American Geriatric Society, 45,* 202-206.

Marson, D. C., Chatterjee, A., Ingram, K. K., & Harrell, L. E. (1996). Toward a neurologic model of competency: Cognitive predictors of capacity to consent in Alzheimer's disease using three different legal standards. *Neurology, 46,* 666-672.

Marson, D. C., Cody, H. A., Ingram, K. K., & Harrell, L. E. (1995). Neuropsychological predictors of competency in Alzheimer's disease using a rational reasons legal standard. *Archives of Neurology, 52,* 955-959.

Marson, D. C., Earnst, K. S., Jamil, F., Bartolucci, A., Harrell, L. E. (2000). Consistency of physicians' legal standard and personal judgments of competency in patients with Alzheimer's disease. *Journal of the American Geriatrics Society, 48,* 911-918.

Marson, D. C., Hawkins, L., McInturff, B., & Harrell, L. E. (1997). Cognitive models that predict physician judgments of capacity to consent in mild Alzheimer's disease. *Journal of the American Geriatrics Society, 45,* 458-464.

Marson, D. C., & Hebert, T.(2005). Civil competencies in older adults with dementia: Medical decision-making capacity, financial capacity, and testamentary capacity. In G.J. Larrabee, (Ed.), *Forensic neuropsychology: A scientific approach* (pp. 334-377).New York: Oxford University Press.

Marson, D. C., & Hebert, T. (2008a). Financial capacity. In B. L. Cutler B.L.(Ed.), *Encyclopedia of psychology and the law,* (Vol. 1, pp. 313-316). Sage Publications.

Marson, D. C., & Hebert, T. (2008b). Testamentary capacity. In B.L. Cutler (Ed.), *Encyclopedia of Psychology and the Law,* (Vol. 2, pp. 798-801). Sage Publications.

Marson, D., Huthwaite, J., & Hebert, K. (2004). Testamentary capacity and undue influence in the elderly: A jurisprudent therapy perspective. *Law and Psychology Review, 28,* 71-96.

Marson, D. C., & Ingram, K. (1996). Competency to consent to research: A growing field of research. *Journal of Ethics, Law, and Aging, 2,* 59-63.

Marson, D. C., Ingram, K., Cody, H. A., & Harrell, L. E. (1995). Assessing the competency of patients with Alzheimer's disease under different legal standards. *Archives of Neurology, 52,* 949-954.

Marson, D. C., McInturff, B., Hawkins, L., Bartolucci, A., & Harrell, L. E. (1997). Consistency of physician judgments of capacity to consent in mild Alzheimer's disease. *The American Geriatrics Society, 45,* 453-457.

Marson, D. C., Sawrie, S., McInturff, B., Snyder, S., Chatterjee, A., Stalvey, T., Boothe, A. & Harrell, L. (2000). Assessing financial capacity in patients with Alzheimer's disease: A conceptual model and prototype instrument. *Archives of Neurology, 57*, 877-884.

Marson, D. C., Schmitt, F. A., Ingram, K. K., & Harrell, L. E. (1994). Determining the competency of Alzheimer patients to consent to treatment and research. *Alzheimer Disease and Associated Disorders, 8*, 5-18.

Martin, R., Griffith, R., Belue, K., Harrell, L., Zamrini, E., Anderson, B., Bartolucci, A., & Marson, D. (2008). Declining financial capacity in patients with mild Alzheimer's disease: A one-year longitudinal study. *American Journal of Geriatric Psychiatry, 16*, 209-219.

Masters, W.H.; & Johnson, V.E. (1966). *Human Sexual Response*. Toronto: Bantam Books.

Matthias, R.E., Lubben, J.E., Atchison, K.A. & Schweitzer, S.O. (1997). Sexual activity and satisfaction among very old adults: results from a community dwelling Medicare population survey, *Gerontologist*, 37, 6-14.

Mayhew, M.. (2005). Survey of state guardianship laws: Statutory provisions for clinical evaluations. *Bifocal, Journal. of the ABA Commission on Law and Aging 26*, 1-19.

McGwin, G., Chapman, V., & Owsley, C. (2000). Visual risk factors for driving difficulty among older drivers. *Accident Analysis & Prevention, 32*, 735-744.

McLuhan, M. (1964). *Understanding Media: The Extensions of Man*. New York: McGraw-Hill.

McPeek, R.M., & Nakayama, K. (1995). Linkage of attention and saccades in visual search task. *Investigative Ophthalmology & Visual Science, 36*, S354.

Meeks, S., & Walker, J. (1990). Blunted affect, blunted lives? Negative symptoms, ADL functioning, and mental health among older adults. *International Journal of Geriatric Psychiatry, 5*, 233-238.

Meisel, A. (1995). *The right to die* (2nd ed.). New York,: Wiley.

Meisel, A. & Cerminara, K. (2008). *The Right to Die: The Law of End-of-Life Decision-making* (3rd ed.). New York: Aspen Publishers.

Meisel, A., Roth, L., & Lidz, C. W. (1977). Toward a model of the legal doctrine of informed consent. *American Journal of Psychiatry, 134*, 285-289.

Mezzullo, L. A., & Woolpert, M. (2004). *Advising the Elderly Client*. St. Paul, MN: Thomson / West.

Milgram, S. (1963). Behavioral study of obedience. *Journal of Abnormal and Social Psychology, 67,* 371-378.

Minnesota Statues Annotated. (1998). § 525.54, subd. 2.

Misra, S., Socherman, R., Park, B. S., Hauser, P., & Ganzini, L. (2008). Influence of mood state on capacity to consent to research in patients with bipolar disorder. *Bipolar Disorder, 10*, 303-309.

Mitrishina, M., Boone, K.B., Razani, J. & D'Elia, L.F. (2005). *Handbook of Normative Data for Neuropsychological Assessment* (2nd ed.). New York: Oxford University Press.

Montgomery County Mediation Center, Institute for the Study of Conflict Transformation & Temple University's Elderly Law Project (2007). Symposium conducted at the meeting of the First National Symposium on Ethical Standards for Elder Mediation, Philadelphia, PA.

Morris, J. (1993). The Clinical Dementia Rating (CDR): Current version and scoring rules. *Neurology, 43,* 2412-2414.

Moye, J. (2003). Guardianship and conservatorship. In T. Grisso (Ed.), *Evaluating competences: Forensic assessments and instruments* (2nd Ed.)(pp. 391-460). New York: Kluwer Academic.

Moye, J., Butz, S. W., Marson, D. C., & Wood, E. (2007). A conceptual model and assessment template for capacity evaluation in adult guardianship. *Gerontologist, 47*, 591–603.

Moye, J., Gurrera, R. J., Karel, M. J., Edelstein, B., & O'Connell, C. (2006). Empirical advances in the assessment of the capacity to consent to medical treatment: Clinical implications and research needs. *Clinical Psychology Review, 26*, 1054-1077.

Moye, J., & Karel, M. J. (1999). Evaluating decisional capacities in older adults: Results of two clinical studies. *Advances in Medical Psychology, 10*, 71-84.

Moye, J., Karel, M. J., Azar, A. R., & Gurrera, R. J. (2004a). Capacity to consent to treatment: Empirical comparison of three instruments in older adults with and without dementia. *The Gerontologist, 44*,166-175.

Moye, J., Karel, M. J., Azar, A. R., & Gurrera, R. J. (2004b). Hopes and cautions for instrument- based evaluations of consent capacity: Results of a construct validity study of three instruments. *Ethics, Law, and Aging Review, 10*, 39-61.

Moye, J., Karel, M. J., Edelstein, B., Hicken, B., Armesto, J. C., & Gurrera, R. J. (2008). Assessment of capacity to consent to treatment: Current research, the "ACCT" approach, future directions. *Clinical Gerontologist, 31*, 37-66.

Moye, J., & Marson, D. C. (2007). Assessment of decision-making capacity in older adults: An emerging area of practice and research. *The Journals of Gerontology Series B: Psychological Science and Social Sciences, 62*, 3-11.

Moye, J., Wood, E., Edelstein, B., Wood, S., Bower, E. H., Harrison, J. A., & Armesto, J.C. (2007). Statutory reform is associated with improved court practice: Results of a tri-state study. *Behavioral Sciences and the Law, 25*, 425-436.

Moye, J., Wood, S., Edelstein, B., Armesto, J. C., Bower, E. H., Harrison, J. A., Wood, E. (2007). Clinical evidence for guardianship of older adults is inadequate: Findings from a tri-state study. *The Gerontologist, 47*, 604-612.

The National Center on Elder Abuse. (1998) *The National Elder Abuse Incidence Study*. Retrieved July 12, 2008 from http://www.aoa.gov/eldfam/Elder_Rights/Elder_Abuse/ ABuseReport_Full.pdf

National Center for Ethics and Healthcare. (2002). *Ten myths about decision-making capacity*. Washington, DC: Author.

National Committee on Uniform Traffic Laws and Ordinances (2000). *Uniform Vehicle Code.* Retrieved on July 20, 2008 from http://www.ncutlo.org/modellaws.htm.

National Conference of Commissioners on Uniform State Laws, Uniform Guardianship and Protective Proceedings Act. Retrieved on March 14, 2008, from: http://www.nccusl.org/nccusl/uniformact_summaries/uniformacts-s-ugappa97.asp

New Hampshire Revised Statues Annotated. (1999). § 464-A:2(XI).

Nolan-Haley, J. M., (2001). *Alternative Dispute Resolution in a Nutshel*. St Paul, MN: West Publishing Company.

Office of the Public Advocate (OPA). (2003). *Mental Capacity and Advance Directives Fact   Sheet 22.* South Australia. Retrieved on March 19, 2008, www.opa.sa.gov.au/documents/09_Publications/Fact_Sheets/22-Mental_Capacity_Advance_Directives.pdf

Okonkwo, O. C., Crowe, M., Wadley, V. G., & Ball, K. (2008). Visual attention and self-regulation of driving among older adults. *International Psychogeriatrics, 20*, 162-173.

Owsley, C., Ball, K., & Keeton, D. M. (1995). Relationship between visual sensitivity and target localization in older adults. *Vision Search, 35*, 579-587.

Owsley, C., Ball, K., McGwin, G. Jr., Sloane, M. E., Roenker, D. L., & White, M. F. (1998). Visual processing impairment and risk of motor vehicle crash among older adults. *Journal of American Medical Association, 279*, 1083-8.

Palmer, B. W., Dunn, L. B., Depp, C. A., Eyler, L. T., & Jeste, D. V. (2007). Decisional capacity to consent to research among patients with bipolar disorder: Comparison with schizophrenia patients and healthy subjects. *Journal of Clinical Psychiatry, 68*, 689-696.

Palmer, B. W., & Salva, G. N. (2007). The association of specific neuropsychological deficits with capacity to consent to research or treatment. *Journal of the International Neuropsychological Society, 13*, 1047-1059.

Parry, J. (1986). Decision-making rights over persons and property. In S.J. Brakel, J. Parry, & B. A. Weiner. (Eds.), *The mentally disabled and the law* (3rd ed., pp. 435-506). Chicago, IL: American Bar Foundation.

Parry, J., & Gilliam, F. P. (2002). *Handbook on mental disability law*. Washington, DC: American Bar Association Commission on Mental and Physical Disability Law.

Pasino, J., & Kahan, J. (2001*). Neuropsychological Screening for Driving Medical Examination Protocol, Rancho Los Amigos National Rehabilitation Center*. Unpublished manuscript.

Patrick, D.L., Pearlman, R. A., Starks, H. E., Cain, K. C., Cole, W. G., & Uhlmann, R. F. (1997). Validation of preferences for life-sustaining treatment: Implications for advance care planning. *Annals of Internal Medicine, 127*, 509-517.

Pearlman, R. A., Cain, K. C., Patrick, D. L., Appelbaum-Maizel, M., Starks, H. E., Jecker, N. S.& Uhlmann, R. F. (1993). Insights pertaining to patient assessments of states worse than death. *Journal of Clinical Ethics, 4*, 33-41.

Persinger v. Holst, 639 N.W.2d 594 (Mich. Ct. App. 2001).

Pierce, P.S. (1989). *Adult functional adaptive behavior scale (AFABS): Manual of directions*. Togus, ME: Author.

Powell, B. V., & Link, R. C. (1994). The sense of a client: Confidentiality issues in representing the elderly. *Fordham Law Review, 1197*, 1234-1238.

Pruchno, R. A., Smyer, M. A., Rose, M. S., Hartman-Stein, P. E., & Laribee-Henderson, D. L. (1995). Competence of long-term care residents to participate in decisions about their medical care: A brief, objective assessment. *The Gerontologist, 35*, 622-629.

Proceedings of the Conference on Ethical Issues in Representing Older Clients: Recommendations of the Conference. (1994). Fordham Law Review, 62, 5.

President's Commission for the Study of Ethical Problems in Medicine and Biomedical and Behavioral Research. (1982). *Report: Making Health Care Decisions: The Ethical and Legal Implications of Informed Consent in the Patient-Practitioner Relationship*. Washington, DC: U.S. Government Printing Office.

Qualls, S. & Smyer, M. (Eds.). (2007). *Changes in Decision-Making Capacity in Older Adults: Assessment and Intervention*. New York: Wiley Series in Clinical Geropsychology.

Quinn, M. J. (2005). *Guardianship of adults: Achieving justice, autonomy, and safety*. New York: Springer Publishing.

Regan, J. J., & Gilfix, M. (2003). *Tax, estate & financial Planning for the elderly: Forms & practice*. New York: Bender.

Reger, M. A., Welsh, R. K., Watson, G. S., Cholerton, B., Baker, L. D., & Craft, S. (2004). The relationship between neuropsychological functioning and driving ability in dementia: A meta-analysis. *Neuropsychology, 18*, 85-93.

Restatement of the Law Second, Contracts. (1981). Philadelphia, PA: American Law Institute.

Richardson, J.P., & Lazur, A. (1995) Sexuality in the nursing home patient. *American Family Physician, 51,* 121-124.

Roenker, D. L., Cissell, G. M., Ball, K. K., Wadley, V. G., & Edwards, J. D. (2003). Speed-of-processing and driving simulator training result in improved driving performance. *Human Factors, 45*, 218-233.

Roter, D., Frankel, R. M., Hall, J., & Sluyter, D. (2006). The expression of emotion through nonverbal behavior in medical visits mechanisms and outcomes. *Journal of General Internal Medicine, 21*, S28–S34.

Roter, D. L., & Hall, J. A. (2004). Physician gender and patient-centered communication: a critical review of empirical research. *Annual Review of Public Health, 25*, 497-519.

Roth, L. H., Meisel, A., & Lidz, C. W. (1977). Tests of competency to consent to treatment. *American Journal of Psychiatry, 134*, 279–284.

Royall, D. R., Cordes, J., & Polk, M. (1997). Executive control and the comprehension of medical information by elderly retirees. *Experimental Aging Research, 23*, 301-313.

Royall, D., R., Lauterbach, E., Kaufer, D., Malloy, P., Coburn, K., & Black, K. (2007). The cognitive correlates of functional status: A review from the Committee on Research of the American

Neuropsychiatric Association. *The Journal of Neuropsychiatry and Clinical Neurosciences, 19*, 249-265.

Ruchinskas, R. (2005). Risk assessment as an integral aspect of capacity evaluations. *Rehabilitation Psychology, 50*, 197-200.

Rush, R. L., & Lank, R. J. (2000). How to thwart financial fraud of elderly clients. *The Wisconsin CPA*, 12-13.

Rutman, D., & Silberfeld, M. (1992). A preliminary report on the discrepancy between clinical and test evaluations of competency. *Canadian Journal of Psychiatry, 37*, 634–639.

Sabatino, C. P. (1996). Competency: Refining our legal fictions. In M.A. Smyer, K. W. Schaie & M.B. Kapp (Eds.), *Older adults decision making and the law* (pp. 1-28). New York: Springer.

Sabatino, C. P., & Basinger, S. L. (2000). Competency: Reforming our legal fictions. *Journal of Mental Health & Aging, 6,* 116-144.

Sabatino, C. P., & Spurgeon, E. D. (2007). Facilitating voting as people age: Implications of cognitive impairment—Introduction. *The McGeorge Law Review, 38*, 843-859.

Sanders, A. F. (1970). Some aspects of the selective process in the functional field of view. *Ergonomics, 13*, 101-117.

Schmand, B., Gouwenberg, B., Smit, J. H., & Jonker, C. (1999). Assessment of mental competency in community-dwelling elderly. *Alzheimer s Disease and Associated Disorders, 13*, 80-87.

Schonwetter, R. S., Walker, R. M., Solomon, M., Indurkhya, A, & Robinson, B. E. (1996). Life values, resuscitation preferences, and the applicability of living wills in an older population. *Journal of American Geriatric Society, 44*, 954-8.

Schultheis, M.T. (February 2007a). *The neuropsychology of driving*. Continuing Education course presented at 35th Annual Meeting of International Neuropsychological Society. Portland, Oregon.

Schultheis, M.T. (April 2007b). *Driving assessment of rehabilitation population*. Presentation at 9th Annual Rehabilitation Psychology Conference. Charlotte, NC.

Scogin, F., & Perry, J. (1986). Guardianship proceedings with older adults: The role of functional assessment and gerontologists. *Law & Psychology Review, 10*, 123-138.

Segal, D. L., Coolidge, F. L., O'Riley, A., & Heinz, B. A. (2006). Structured and semi-structured interviews. In M. Hersen (Ed.), *Clinician s handbook of adult behavioral assessment* (pp. 121-144). Boston: Elsevier Academic Press.

Shulman, K.I., Cohen, C.A., Kirsh, F.C., Hull, I.M., & Champine, P.R. (2007). Assessment of testamentary capacity and vulnerability to undue influence. *American Journal of Psychiatry, 164,* 722-727

Singer, M.S. (1993). Undue Influence and written documents: Psychological Aspects. *Cultic Studies Journal, 10,* (1) 19-32.

Smyer, M. A., Schaie, K. W., & Kapp, M. B. (Eds.). (1996). *Older adults decision-making and the law*. New York: Springer.

Spar, J. E., & Garb, A. S. (1992). Assessing competency to make a will. *American Journal of Psychiatry, 149*, 169-174.

Staats, N., & Edelstein, B. (1995). *Cognitive changes associated with the declining competency of older adults*. Paper presented at the Gerontological Society of America, Los Angeles.

Stanley, B., Stanley, M., Guido, J., & Garvin, L. (1988). The functional competency of elderly at risk. *The Gerontologist, 28, supplement*, 53-58.

Starr, T. J., Pearlman, R. A., & Uhlmann, R. F. (1986). Quality of life and resuscitation decisions in elderly patients. *Journal of General Internal Medicine, 1*, 373–379.

Stavis, P. F. (1991). Sexual activity and the law of consent. *Quality of Care Newsletter, 50*. Retrieved on March 14, 2008, from: www.cqcapd.state.ny.us/counsels_corner/cc50.htm

Stavis, P. F., & Walker-Hirsch, L. W. (1999). Consent to sexual activity. In R. D. Dinerstein, S. S. Herr, & J. L. O'Sullivan (Eds.), *A guide to consent.* (pp. 57-67). Washington, DC: American Association for Mental Deficiency.

Strauss, E., Sherman. E.M.S., Spreen, O. (2006). *A Compendium of Neuropsychological Tests: Administration, Norms, and Commentary* (3rd ed.). New York. Oxford University Press.

Stuck, A. E., Walthert, J. M., Nikolaus, T., Bula, C. J., Hohmann, C., & Beck, J. C. (1999). Risk factors for functional status decline in community-living elderly people: A systemic literature review. *Social Science & Medicine, 48*, 445-469.

Sturman, E. D. (2005). The capacity to consent to treatment and research: A review of standardized assessment tools. *Clinical Psychology Review, 25*, 954-974.

Sundram, C. J., & Stavis, P. F. (1993). Sexual behavior and mental retardation. *Mental and Physical Disabilities Law Reporter, 17*, 448-457.

Taub, H. A., Baker, M. T., Kline, G. E., & Sturr, J. F. (1987). Comprehension of informed consent by young-old and old-old volunteers. *Experimental Aging Research, 13*, 173-178.

Tatemichi, T. K., Desmond, D. W., Stern, Y., Paik, M., & Bagiella, E. (1994). Cognitive impairment after stroke: Frequency, patterns, and relationship to functional abilities. *Journal of Neurology, Neurosurgery, and Psychiatry, 57*, 202-207.

Teaster, P., Wood, E., Schmidt, Jr., W. C., & Lawrence, S. A. (2007). *In the best interest of incapacitated people: Public guardianship after 25 years*. Washington, DC: University of Kentucky and ABA Commission on Law and Aging.

Tomoda, A., Yasumiya, R., Sumiyama, T., Tankada, K., Hayakawa, T., Kimimori, M. (1997). Reliability and validity of structured interview for competency incompetency assessment testing and ranking inventory. *Journal of Clinical Psychology, 53*, 443-450.

Tomoda, A., Yasumiya, R., Sumiyama, T., & Tsukada, K. (1997). Validity and reliability of structured interview for competency incompetency assessment testing and ranking inventory. *Journal of Clinical Psychology, 53*, 443.

Tueth, M. J. (2000). Exposing financial exploitation of impaired elderly persons. *American Journal of Geriatric Psychiatry, 8*, 104-111.

Uhlmann, R. F., & Pearlmann, R. A. (1991). Perceived quality of life and preferences for life-sustaining treatment in older adults. *Archives of Internal Medicine, 151*, 495–497.

Uhlmann, R. F., Pearlman, R., & Cain, K. (1988). Physician and spouse predictions of elderly patients' resuscitation preferences. *Journal of Gerontology, 43*, 115-121.

Uniform Guardianship and Protective Proceedings Act § 102(5) (1997). Retrieved on March 14, 2008, from: http://www.law.upenn.edu/bll/ulc/ fnact99/1990s/ugppa97.htm

Uniform Health-Care Decisions Act of 1993, § 1(3) (1994). Retrieved on March 14, 2008, from: http://www.law.upenn.edu/bll/archives/ulc/fnact99/1990s/uhcda93.htm

U.S. Department of Motor Vehicles. (n.d.). Retrieved on March 14, 2008, from: www.dmv.gov

U.S. Department of Veterans Affairs. (1997). *Assessment of competency and capacity of the older adult: A practice guideline for psychologists*. Milwaukee, WI: National Center for Cost Containment. (NTIS No. PB97-147904).

Vellinga, A., Smit, J. H., van Leeuwen, E., van Tilburg, W., & Jonker, C. (2004). Competence to consent to treatment of geriatric patients: Judgments of physicians, family members and the vignette method. *International Journal of Geriatric Psychiatry, 19*, 645.

Wallace, M. (2003). Sexuality and aging in long-term care. *Annals of Long-Term Care, 11*, 53-59.

Waller, J. A. (1980). Physician's role in highway safety: Functional impairment in driving. *New York State Journal of Medicine, 80*, 1987-91.

Walsh, A. C. et al. (1994). *Mental capacity: Legal and medical aspects of assessment and treatment* (2nd ed.). Colorado Springs, CO: McGraw-Hill.

Wan, H., Sengupta, M. Velkoff, V. A., & Debarros, K. A. (2005). *U. S. Census Bureau, current publication reports, 65+ in the United States: 2005*. Washington, DC: U. S. Government Printing Office. Retrieved on March 5, 2008, from: http://www.census.gov/prod/2006pubs/p23-209.pdf

Wertheimer, A. (2003). *Consent to sexual relations*. Cambridge United Kingdom : Cambridge University Press.

Wong, J. G., Clare, I. C. H., Holland, A. J., Watson, P. C., & Gunn, M. (2000). The capacity of people with a "mental disability" to make a health care decision. *Psychological Medicine, 30*, 295-306.

Wood, E. (2001). Dispute resolution and dementia: Seeking solutions. *Georgia Law Review, 35*, 785.